# THE WELL ADJUSTED DOG

"You take your dog to the vet, and expect him to feel better fast. But if your pet's back is hurting or spine needs adjusting, you're out of luck—most states do not allow chiropractors to work on animals, and only a handful of veterinarians know anything about chiropractic, says Dr. Daniel Kamen, expert on treating anything from sedated lions to llamas. He'll tell you why pet owners should adjust their own dogs' backs, and how to do it."                                        —*Radio & TV Report* (1996)

"Sorry, he won't do giraffes anymore—but if your dog, cat or horse has a back out of whack, Dr. Daniel Kamen is your man."
                                                                    —*Star* (1987)

"An Illinois chiropractor is using his skills on animals, and he says the technique works as well on dogs, cats, and horses as it does on humans. An added benefit, says Dr. Daniel R. Kamen of Buffalo Grove, is that four-legged patients don't talk back."
                                                                    —*Insight* (1986)

"Kamen is a chiropractor with a twist. His main occupation is treating people with back or arthritic problems. However, his sideline is treating animals. He has treated a giraffe, a lion, a bear, a monkey, and several cats, horses and dogs... 'Admittedly, there isn't a big calling for lion chiropractors,' said Kamen. 'You just don't find that many lions or bears in the suburbs.'"
                                                    —*Countryside ReminderNews* (1984)

"Though he wants to steer clear of legal beagles, Kamen argued, 'We have evidence that chiropractic works on humans. Animals have similar nervous systems and spines, so I believe chiropractic would help them too.'" —*Chicago Sun-Times* (1982)

# The
# Well Adjusted Dog
## Canine Chiropractic Methods YOU Can Do

by Dr. Daniel R. Kamen, D.C.

**BROOKLINE BOOKS**

Illustrations ©1996 by Amy Sibiga.
Ink renditions of D.D. and B.J. Palmer ©1996 by Jeffrey Kamen.
Cover art and design by Julia Sedykh.
Interior design and typography by Erica L. Schultz.

**Disclaimer (to dog owners or anyone else who reads this book):** This book is about managing vertebral subluxations in dogs, not treating disease. Do not use this book in place of veterinary care. All health questions concerning your dog, including those pertaining to the use of chiropractic care, must initially be addressed by your veterinarian.

The author or anyone and anything associated with the writing, production or distribution of this book assumes **ABSOLUTELY NO** liability to or for anyone (man or beast) who uses the information presented in this book. The reader or user of the information presented in this book assumes the entire responsibility and liability for his or her actions.

 **PRINTED IN CANADA**

10 9 8 7 6 5 4 3 2

International Standard Book Number: 1-57129-030-3
Library of Congress Catalog Card Number: 96-90279

*Published by*
**BROOKLINE BOOKS**
P.O. Box 1047 • Cambridge, MA 02238-1047
*Order toll-free:* 1-800-666-BOOK

# Contents

*Dogs of the world, prepare to be healthier through chiropractic. Your owner has purchased this book for you. Next to a steak, this is the best present you can receive!*

\* \* \*

A variety of talents and personalities made this book a reality. I'd like to mention a few of them and acknowledge their contributions—even though some would rather remain anonymous.

- The Illinois Department of Professional Regulation (they police and license me and all other doctors in Illinois). Without them, not only would this book not have been possible, it wouldn't have been necessary.
- The American Veterinary Medical Association (AVMA). The "AMA" of veterinarians has its national office in Schaumburg, Illinois, which is a ten-minute drive from my office. I want to personally thank them for refusing me access to their library with its vast resources which I could have used for research purposes. I know that I am a chiropractor and not an AVMA member. You could have been a little nicer.
- My father, Jack Kamen, M.D. For had he sneezed during the time of my conception, I would have been somebody else altogether. (But I would have granted permission for a certain chiropractor to use the AVMA library.)
- My mother, Shirley D. Kamen (Hen). Her incredible paintings, which decorate my office, created the per-

fect writing environment.

- My wife, Sharon. I guess every family has to have at least one levelheaded member.
- My sons, Jeffrey, Gary, and Kevin. All talented, smart, and good-looking! Was there ever a doubt!
- Ken Kirby and Steve Loring, two computer experts who saved me at least a thousand hours.
- Dr. Ron Neuerburg, D.C. The ideas you gave me were brilliant. Eldora, Iowa, is blessed with your presence.
- Ron Stringer for a fine editing job.
- Amy Sibiga, a true professional artist, for her talent and skill in creating the drawings presented in this book.
- The Palmer College of Chiropractic. Without you, chiropractic would not have flourished and the world would have been an unhealthier place.
- My special friends, Dr. Alan Perkins and Michelle, *Perfect* Perkins and Judy. Thanks for your help. Your dogs are great.
- Dr. Greg Linn, whose wisdom and ability to communicate solid and sensible ideas was greatly appreciated.
- Sadi Ranson and Milton Budoff of Brookline Books for having faith in me and creating more awareness for animal chiropractic.

# Preface

The time has come for animal chiropractic to be recognized for what it is; a powerful healthcare practice that can help animals achieve a higher level of well being, which is not always available through traditional allopathic methods.

Animal chiropractic has always had an identity crisis. Many people don't know it exists, or of its miraculous health benefits. There aren't any officially recognized animal chiropractors, because there is no place on this earth where someone can get a "degree" for its practice (veterinarians can practice it if they want, but most choose not to). State laws prohibit licensed chiropractors from practicing on animals, and chiropractic is not taught in veterinary schools. What a shame. Chiropractic care is often the only way to help the most stubborn health conditions. I simply refuse to keep canine chiropractic methods a secret from dog owners. And dog owners, I am told, can practice chiropractic on their own pet, thus forcing the need for a book of this nature.

Maybe this book will relieve some of the frustration a dog owner has when their dog is repeatedly denied chiropractic care because their local chiropractor fears for his or her license.

Your dog has rights!

— *Daniel R. Kamen, B.A., D.C.*

# INTRODUCTION

# ONE FINE MORNING (THE PERILS AND PITFALLS OF ANIMAL CHIROPRACTIC)

On April 18, 1990, my phone rang at 6:09 A.M. "Hello?" I said in my gravelly morning voice. I was sleeping on the couch, the TV still blaring after a night watching *All in the Family* reruns.

"Is this Dr. Kamen?" screeched the voice on the other end. Naturally, I assumed it was a patient with a hot lumbar.

"Yes, this is he," I said, while picking up the phone that I had just knocked off the end table.

"Heeeeeey Doc, this is Johnny Brandmeier, and you're live on 'the Loop.' I'd like to ask you about the article I saw in the *Sun-Times* yesterday."

No big deal, I thought. I've been interviewed live before. I've appeared on *The Late Show with Arsenio Hall*, *Good Morning America*, and local radio and TV shows. Johnny B., a popular radio host on Chicago's WLUP, was making a name for himself by being shocking and controversial. Well, I've made a living being put on the spot. When you're a chiropractor, you're often asked to explain yourself. Why it works. If it works. Are you now or have you ever been a chiropractor?

"Yes," I said, "I read that article. Isn't that a slick-looking picture of me bending over a horse's tush?"

"Well, Doc," Mr. B. said with all the sincerity of *Godfather II*'s Michael Corleone when he kissed his brother Fredo, "we heard that the State of Illinois has made some inquiries about your work with animals."

None of this was news to me. As I mentioned, I've been up against the media before. Johnny B's main intention was to corner me into a confession that I was indeed working on animals in Illinois. Anyone who is a licensed chiropractor in Illinois—or for that matter, in most states—is strictly forbidden to practice on animals. That would be practicing veterinary medicine without a license. The penalty for this breach of the law is a stiff fine or revocation of your license. Also, a licensed chiropractor cannot disassociate himself from his license; in other words, he or she cannot, as a favor to a friend, visit a house or a farm and adjust an animal's spine.

Although a lay person can legally do just about anything he wants to his own pet, including chiropractic manipulation, with fewer than two hundred chiropractors and veterinarians in the U.S. performing chiropractic manipulation on animals, it is nearly impossible for the average dog or horse owner to find one who does. And inasmuch as the fine for a chiropractor exceeds five hundred dollars for each infraction, who's going to stick his neck out? Meanwhile, most veterinarians are too busy setting broken legs and treating infections to learn how to perform chiropractic adjustments.

I am not afraid to admit that I work on animals. It's actually getting caught in the act that will jeopardize my livelihood. It's not easy for someone to prove you've adjusted an animal. Unless you're a clumsy ox, the chiropractic adjustment leaves no marks, and no evidence in the blood or urine. Sneaking around has been the norm for most chiropractors who wish to treat animals. It's a shame it has to be this way. A sorely needed service is thereby kept from the public.

I was reluctant to go into all this with Mr. B. I like animals. I like helping animals. I don't like people getting in my way when I'm only trying to help.

But before I could get in another word, Johnny interrupted me to introduce a veterinarian from the American Veterinary Medical Association, which just happens to have their national headquarters in Schaumburg, Illinois, ten miles from my office. Even though I have tremendous respect for veterinarians, I find it annoying trying to communicate with closed minds, and the Good Vet was very closed-minded.

"So," said Johnny B., "we have Dr. Kamen, the animal chiropractor, on the line. I understand that Illinois does not want Dr. Kamen to practice on animals. How do you feel about this?"

"The state is right," the Good Vet pronounced. "In order to practice medicine on animals in Illinois you must be a licensed veterinarian. Period."

I couldn't believe my ears. "Chiropractic," I suggested, "is a drugless healing art that enables the body to use its natural recuperative abilities to heal itself."

The Good Vet simply repeated himself: "A chiropractor may *not* treat animals in Illinois."

Johnny started to get excited. This was just what he wanted—a confrontation, for the sake of the ratings. Frankly, I'm a simple person with average abilities and intelligence. I don't like fights. I can handle coming home every day to three healthy (knock on wood), screaming children, but arguing on the phone at six in the morning with a narcissistic prima donna is intolerable.

So I baited a trap. I asked the Good Vet if he would at least allow me the privilege of adjusting a deer's neck if I saw a lame one in the woods. "Absolutely not!" he pontificated.

"All right, then," I continued. "I want you to carefully think about this question. You just said I couldn't adjust a deer, implying that I wasn't qualified in some way because I'm not licensed by the state. So what would you say if I got a shotgun and a hunting license and approached this deer with the sore neck. Would you rather I adjust its neck or shoot its head off? Or maybe you'd like it better if I shot its head off first, then adjusted its neck! Which'll it be? And remember, if you're in private practice some of your patients are probably listening."

Now, I know my argument didn't hold water. I was merely pointing out how ridiculous the laws are. Anyone with a gun and two hundred bucks for a hunting license can saunter into the woods and legally maim a deer. God forbid I should try to *help* the poor thing!

Well, all hell broke loose. The Good Vet never answered me, because Johnny started howling about how his switchboard was lighting up. Callers wanted to talk to me about their pets. Some of them wanted to curse me. By this time, my kids were up and hollering. The Johnny B. show was on full blast in the kitchen. My wife, Sharon (bless her for putting up with me), was itemizing my carpool detail for the day. I dropped the receiver into its cradle. So that was my wake-up call.

As I headed for work that morning after dropping off one of my boys at school, I tuned my car radio to "the Loop." As I attempted to balance a cup of lukewarm White Hen coffee and a doughnut (I'm no health nut), I heard my name again, this time as mentioned by a local chiropractor who has something against me and my modest notoriety for working on animals. He's telling everyone how much of a goof I was on TV with Arsenio Hall, how I oversimplified chiropractic to make it sound like a weekend seminar. "So what?" I thought. "I can take criticism—I've been married nearly eighteen years!" But his attitude gnawed at me. We chiropractors are our own worst enemy. The American Medical Association is wasting its time trying to destroy us. Give us another ten years, and we'll do it ourselves.

I turned off the radio and put on a music tape to soothe my nerves. I got to my office ahead of my first patient, which is unusual for me. Katie had already been there for fifteen minutes.

"The phone hasn't stopped ringing since I walked in," she said.

"Who's been calling?" I asked.

"Er... were you on the radio today?" she asked.

"Yes," I said. "Johnny Brandmeier woke me up this morning to do an interview about yesterday's *Sun-Times* article. And I have a feeling I'm not going to come out of this unscathed."

My first patient of the day, Mrs. Fritch, hobbled in for her morning appointment. In fairly good health for her eighty years,

Mrs. Fritch is the old-fashioned bun-in-the-hair type of granny who doesn't like too much excitement—the sort who has church-organ music following her around wherever she goes. I escorted her to Room 1, closest to the waiting room. She positioned herself on the adjusting table and waited for me to go to work. It was a routine treatment. Mrs. Fritch has a long history of low-back pain, and getting adjusted is her only form of relief. Upon completion of the treatment, she was feeling relaxed and ready for the day. I stepped on the pedal that powers the adjusting table and raised her to her feet. She gingerly started walking out of the treatment room and into the reception area to schedule another appointment.

As she was saying her goodbyes, a cat darted out from under a waiting-room chair and startled her so much that she screamed and stepped on the cat's tail at the same time. The cat let out a murderous "Raaaaaw!" and ducked under the chair.

Mrs. Fritch sat down and tried to compose herself.

I looked at Katie. "Why didn't you tell me there was a cat here?"

"I didn't know until now," Katie said.

What had happened, apparently, is that a lady who had heard me on the radio that morning had decided to make an unscheduled visit to my office. She had walked in the front door, past the front desk, and into the bathroom. She had put her cat down outside the bathroom door, and the feline had made its way back to the waiting room. Upon hearing all the commotion, the lady ran to see what had happened. "Bashful!" she panted. "Are you all right?"

Bashful was fine, but Mrs. Fritch had almost had a coronary. I took her back to the treatment room to recuperate for half an hour. I told the cat lady she couldn't bring pets into the office, but that I would be more than happy to examine Bashful outside. She picked up the cat, sat it back on the floor and watched it walk.

"Bashful's fine now, she told me. "She was limping this morning, but she looks fine now."

Mrs. Fritch didn't know it, but she had accidentally performed her first chiropractic adjustment, without so much as a lesson. My guess is that Bashful had a hind-leg or hip misalignment, which was put back into place when he jerked his paw back in response to the pinch of Mrs. Fritch's shoe.

Fortunately, the whole day was not this chaotic. The cat lady was our only unscheduled visitor. But the phone rang for hours with inquiries about my animal services. I didn't accept any animal patients that day. Unless I get a referral from someone I know, I won't accept an animal case at all.

The following day was a different story. After fielding a good number of phone inquires about animals and chiropractic, Katie walked in on the middle of an adjustment. She had a ghastly ashen look on her face.

"What?" I asked, thinking that she might have swallowed her gum.

"Some people are here for you," she answered.

"Who?" I whispered.

"They say they're from the Department of Professional Regulation. They would like to ask you about your 'animal practice.'"

"Tell them just a minute."

I must have a hundred pictures of me posing with patients' dogs, horses, cats, birds, and cows, all of them hanging in my office next to my Palmer College of Chiropractic diploma and my state chiropractic license. It took me under a minute to pull them all down and shove them under my desk. I don't know why I was suddenly frightened. I had been on so many news shows lately, the state had to know something was up. I remembered them making telephone and mail inquiries years before, but nothing had ever come of it. Now, when I was approached by them in person, I panicked.

I picked up the phone. "You can send them back now, Katie." I sat at my desk with a chessboard all set up to play. (Chess has always helped me relax.) Two businesslike women, each about 35 years old, walked in. They were pleasant-looking, not at all intimidating.

"Care for a game of chess?" I cracked.

"No, thank you," said one of the women. "We want to know about the *Sun-Times* article."

I looked around the room at all the empty picture hooks that were still stuck in the wall. Talk about DNA evidence! Amazingly, they didn't notice.

"Oh, that," I said. "The picture in the paper doesn't do the horse justice."

Not terribly amused, the other woman asked, "We'd like to know what it means."

"It means," I said, "that I made a trip to Maywood Park to visit a friend. Nothing more."

"No?" she said skeptically. "What about you treating that horse? What about that?"

"I admit to nothing," I said. "Go ask the horse."

The Untouchables badgered me for only five minutes. And I admitted nothing. I learned long ago that even if you're caught in the act, deny it and put the burden of proof on your accuser. As it turned out, they left without telling me what they intended to do. I reached for a pad and pencil, and peered out the window as they pulled away. I'd had a notion to jot down their license number. It paid off.

For about five weeks after the *Sun-Times* article, I was still receiving calls from people wanting to know about animal chiropractic treatments. This was normal. Sometimes I get a dozen or more calls in one week—even with no new publicity.

But something about one of the calls sent up a red flag. A lady kept on calling me about her beagle. She begged me several times to come out to her place and adjust "Polly." It just didn't feel right, so I kept putting her off. She offered me an outrageous sum of money ($500) if I would come to her house just once. No one had ever done this before. It wasn't too difficult to smell a rat. I continued to say no.

During these weeks I noticed, but paid little attention to, a car that was regularly parked at the automotive service station across from my office. One day, pursuing a hunch, I decided to look for the piece of paper with the Untouchables' license number. Bingo!

Finally, late one afternoon, I spotted someone in the car. I walked over to the car and immediately recognized her as one of the Department of Professional Regulation's sleuths. She rolled down her window. I leaned down and asked her if she could direct me to Dr. Kamen's chiropractic office. "I have a dog with a weak back," I continued. "Do you know how long he's had a weak back?" Then, borrowing a line from the Three Stooges, "Oh, about a week back!"

The women in the car didn't respond—no laughing, no hissing, no nothing. I calmly walked back to my office and looked out the window. A few minutes later, the Department lady drove off, and that was the last I saw of her or her car.

I've often been asked why I even bother with animals. I have a successful human practice, and I make a good living. My answer is always the same. I enjoy it. Life is too short to constantly worry about what other people—including the state authorities—think.

I know a lot of chiropractors who are intimidated by state laws. During my fifteen years of experience with animals, I've had to turn down countless potential animal patients because I was under the scrutiny of a state investigator. At this point in time, it would benefit lay people to learn basic to moderately advanced chiropractic "moves" (i.e., procedures) they can safely perform on their pets when a professional is not available.

Finally, I would like to do my part to dispel a misconception about chiropractic, and one of the best ways to do this is with reference to animals. When a dog or horse is helped by chiropractic, the old placebo theory doesn't wash. In other words, you don't have to *believe* in chiropractic. Chiropractic is not a religion. It's true that up until the last five years, most of the evidence that chiropractic works was based on anecdotal material—that is, on millions of successful clinical results! What could be more convincing?

But with the AMA and the media always breathing down

our backs, we feel compelled to give them a scientific answer. And we *will* give them a scientific answer on how chiropractic works—as soon as they give us a scientific answer on how aspirin works!

# Chapter 1

# Notes on the History of Animal Chiropractic

When a janitor named Harvey Lillard stepped into an old and musty office in the Midwestern river city of Davenport, Iowa, he walked into history. It was 1895, the year chiropractic was born. Founding father Daniel David (D.D.) Palmer (Fig. 1-1), a Canadian-born magnetic healer, discovered the chiropractic principle by accident after Mr. Lillard complained of hearing loss. Seventeen years earlier, Mr. Lillard told him, he had felt a snap in the back of his neck while lifting something at work, and had been almost stone deaf since then. Detecting a misaligned vertebra in back of Mr. Lillard's neck, D.D. Palmer snapped it into place, and Mr. Lillard's hearing soon improved.

Following this startling discovery, D.D. Palmer wondered whether adjusting the spine might not be the key to curing other ailments. He knew there were direct and indirect spinal-nerve links to all the body's organs. Therefore, he reasoned, a pinched spinal nerve leading to the stomach might lead to gastrointestinal conditions, and so on with all the other spinal-nerve-to-organ connections.

Fig. 1-1.
D.D. Palmer.

Fig. 1-2.
B.J. Palmer.

Apocryphal or not, the above story is the chief reason why the chiropractic profession has been the object of the medical community's incessant ridicule, most of which originally stemmed from irresponsible publicity surrounding this story. Claims of deaf cures were advertised throughout the Midwest. People flocked to Davenport to see the new "miracle healer."

The word "chiropractic"—a composite of the Greek *cheir* (hand) and *praktos* (done), hence "done by hand"—was also born in 1895. The Palmer School of Chiropractic was created in the same year, and the profession soon began to flourish. However, it wasn't until D.D.'s son, Bartlett Joshua (B.J.) Palmer (Fig. 1-2), began to practice that chiropractic became a household word, thanks to his charismatic style and business savvy. Unfortunately, outrageous claims of curing everything short of rigor mortis tarnished the credibility of an incredible discovery.

Early chiropractors were often

jailed for practicing medicine without a license. This was clearly an attempt by organized medicine to derail the young profession's momentum. Still, chiropractors thrived. The public wanted an alternative to drugs and surgery. Today, all fifty states license chiropractors, thanks in part to the sophistication and quality of chiropractic educational institutions. It takes at least six years of rigorous training to become a licensed chiropractor. **Note:** Chiropractic is also practiced worldwide. Most of the chiropractors who practice in other countries were educated here, but several fine chiropractic schools are located in various parts of the world including Europe, Japan, Australia, and Canada.

Unsurprisingly, the first chiropractor to practice on animals was D.D. Palmer. Along with his son B.J., he organized within the Palmer School of Chiropractic a course in animal adjusting, and even printed a two-color diploma to issue to those who might complete a comprehensive one-month course of study (Fig. 1-3). Although my search of the literature has produced no evidence of anyone actually receiving one of these DCV (Doctor of Chiropractic Veterinary) diplomas, the Palmer College of Chiropractic (previously the Palmer School of Chiropractic) has a copy of this document in their archives. Also uncertain is the year this course was offered, although it is generally accepted that D.D. Palmer adjusted animals and taught his techniques around the turn of the century. (D.D. died in 1913 at age 68; B.J. died in 1961 at age 78).

Early chiropractors practiced on animals primarily in order to arrive at a proof of the central feature of their new science, the subluxation theory, i.e., that a pinched spinal nerve caused "dis-ease" in the corresponding organ or function. During the

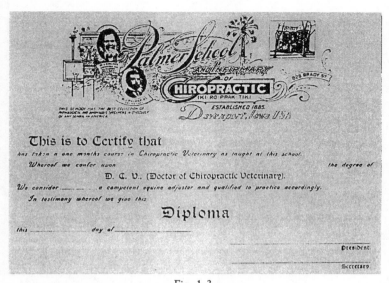

Fig. 1-3.
One of a kind early chiropractic/veterinary diploma (about 1921 or earlier).

beginning years of the profession, B.J. Palmer wanted to demonstrate that the adjustment had more than a placebo effect, as had been charged by the medical community. Unfortunately, the clinical accounts of his successes with animals were largely anecdotal, and B.J.'s work on animals has all but been ignored. To make matters worse, the *Journal of the American Medical Association* stated in its issue of September 17, 1921, "If chiropractors are wise they will confine their malpractice to humans; it is safer." This quip was printed after the AMA learned that Palmer School graduates were working on animals. The article continued, "That men ignorant of the body and its processes should treat the ailments of men, women and children is apparently a small thing; human life is the only thing involved. But that ignoramuses should trifle with the health of a horse or a hog is an outrage; that is property."

Despite the AMA's efforts to discredit the profession and protect the lower life forms, animal studies have often been used to bolster the subluxation theory. When an animal died, the cause of death—such as heart failure, liver, kidney disease, and so on—would be determined. Then a surgical dissection of the spine was made to see if there was any spinal-nerve impingement linked to the animal's condition. And indeed, there often appeared to be a connection between the diseased organ and the corresponding impingement.

Even as the AMA demanded proof of the subluxation theory, it refused to approve any sort of chiropractic activity, including scientific experiments. And while the AMA has never had the legal authority to control the practice of chiropractic, its opinions have always carried enormous political weight, which translates into public opinion. Chiropractors are often asked whether they are now accepted by the AMA, and the answer is always the same: "It doesn't matter." The AMA is a private professional association that sets standards of practice for its members—M.D.'s, not D.C.'s.

The discovery of chiropractic in 1895 created a new element on the health-care periodic table. The first reaction of Western medicine was to purge this beast from the forest. But as the years passed, the medical community has had to acknowledge that chiropractic is here to stay. Even chiropractors themselves started to believe they were here to stay! The reason?

Results. As long as sick people and animals continue to get well, chiropractors will be in demand.

Recently, there has been a proliferation of well-documented scientific research that deeply investigates all the components that add up to the subluxation theory. The research includes studies in biomechanics (joint and muscle movement), comparing the effects of soft to moderate thrusting (i.e., the "adjustment") and the effect it may have on its target, such as an internal organ or muscle. The analogy has been made to a light switch: by turning on the spinal nerve, you light up the organ. It's up to the chiropractor to find the "switch" in the spine and turn it back on.

There is still relatively little literature available on animal chiropractic, however. This is partly due to the fact that chiropractors, as compared to M.D.'s, have always struggled to keep themselves afloat financially, and have therefore had almost no time to work for extra credit. And while veterinarians have always had more than enough to do treating the everyday emergencies that arise in their practices, chiropractors have had more than enough to do just holding onto their licenses to practice. Because most states do not allow chiropractors to work on animals, animal chiropractic remains a closet profession.

One of the early animal chiropractors was Dr. Myles A. Medford, born in 1926 and still going strong. Dr. Medford was discouraged by his experience studying veterinary medicine: he didn't like the huge classrooms or the staff shortages at Coffeyville College in Kansas, and besides, a medical education was expensive. This turned out to be a lucky stroke for animal chiropractic. After attending the Palmer School, Dr. Medford began adjusting animals in 1954 and is recognized as a pioneer in the field, having organized a series of one-on-one workshops with other chiropractors and developed many of the current adjusting techniques. He still maintains a refreshingly youthful enthusiasm regarding the future of animal chiropractic.

In a thought-provoking man-versus-beast comparison, Dr. Medford once stated, "Chiropractic adjustments of the animal kingdom can and do release much more nerve force in quadrupeds than in man. This is due to man allowing his educated intelligence to rule his existence. Educated intelligence in man has all too often overruled the simple rules of innate" ("innate" being synonymous with "life energy"). In other words, Dr. Medford doesn't believe in animal hypochondriacs, whereas people can be talked into—or talk themselves into—believing they're sick. (Every time we learned about a new disease in school, someone in our class would come down with it the next day!) Conversely, animals don't have to believe in chiropractic in order for it to work.

At present, none of the fifty states allows chiropractors to practice on animals (some states allow chiropractors to adjust animals when supervised by a veterinarian). However, a growing number of veterinarians are taking a second look at the benefits of chiropractic for animals. The wave of the times is, after all, natural health care. Given the choice, the informed health-care consumer would rather treat his or her body with pure food, clean water, and exercise than be mistreated with chemicals and the high cost of trying to compensate for an unhealthy lifestyle.

Domesticated animals would surely make the same choice if they could. It is up to us to see that there *is* a choice.

# CHAPTER 2

# THE SUBLUXATION

**Chiropractic Definition of a Vertebral Subluxation:** The physiological and neurological disturbances caused by two adjacent vertebrae pinching a spinal nerve and its related structures. In other words, a vertebra misaligned on top of another vertebra will cause pinching of the spinal nerve in between.

A vertebral subluxation reflects the body's desperate need to respond and adapt to adverse mechanical, chemical, or mental stimuli. The organ victimized by these stimuli—let's say the stomach—will try to send an emergency SOS via the spinal cord to the brain. However, this neurological signal will be blunted by tight spinal muscles gripping and choking the vertebrae that house the spinal nerve belonging to the stomach, thus impairing the "cable" and robbing the stomach of neurological impulses. This, in turn, requires other organs to "make up the slack," thereby creating a tremendous strain on the entire system.

## WHY SUBLUXATIONS?

I'd like to start this discussion by acknowledging the medical doctors and pharmaceutical companies for being the world's foremost supporters of chiropractic. Without their generous and most enthusiastic support, my ability to make a living would be greatly diminished. All of the figures aren't in as of this writing, but a rough estimate is that drug companies alone spend approximately $2.6 billion each year fueling my profession, not quite ten dollars per year per U.S. citizen.

If this sounds facetious, that's because it is. But facts are facts, and the facts are as follows:

The number one cause of subluxations in humans is poisoning. In animals, it's a combination of poisons (toxins in food and annual vaccines) and their athletic lifestyle. Many poisons are made from chemicals, and most of the chemicals we ingest are drugs that were originally designed to help us. Naturally, there is a lot to be said about the progress of pharmacological science. Medical doctors and pharmaceutical companies do save lives and improve the quality of life. But the Food and Drug Administration (FDA) has only required over-the-counter (OTC) drug testing (for effectiveness) since 1962. Among the 500 products the FDA tested in 1962, 75% of them were deemed unsafe or ineffective for their intended use.[1] Even though the FDA has made great strides in protecting our safety, I don't feel even they can provide adequate safeguards from potentially harmful modern drugs. It would serve us well if we all periodically contacted the FDA to get a copy of their product withdraw list (marketed drugs that are no longer considered safe).

Fortunately, your body is equipped with an internal regulator known as "innate intelligence." Be it spiritual or simply a

[1] Kittredge, Mary. *Prescription and Over-The-Counter Drugs*. Chelsea House Publishers, 1989; pp. 62-63.

biological function, innate intelligence gives your body the ability to recognize and metabolically react to a crisis and maintain homeostasis ("all systems go"). A good way to disturb your system is to subluxate it by giving it drugs. A better way is to become *addicted* to drugs.

Cigarette smokers know only too well how addictive nicotine is. When a person first starts to smoke, his body rebels, attempting to purge the cigarette toxins by coughing, sweating, or otherwise eliminating the drug. If the person persists in taking the drug, the body—anticipating more toxins—begins to form an antidote to the poison.

The body seeks to maintain balance at all times. When you're overheated, you begin to perspire. Your internal thermostat is always at work. Likewise, when you continue to smoke, your body continues to manufacture the antidote to the effects of nicotine, thus maintaining homeostasis. (Ah, but what if you decide to quit? In the absence of poison, your body continues to produce the antidote, again upsetting the balance.) The more poison you take, the more antidotes your body makes, and the more your body has to adjust if you decide to quit smoking.

Fortunately, your system can wash out its own antidote in short order, usually in about four days. In other words, cigarette smokers are just four days away from ridding themselves of the physical addiction of nicotine. Most people who return to smoking do so not because of physical cravings, but because of force of habit, unresolved stress, and the fear of gaining weight.

Subluxations are also caused by drugs that are not considered addictive, but still deregulate the body. The repeated use of enemas, for example, will make you dependent on them. By resorting to enemas, you are essentially taking away the intestine's job, punishing it for arriving late to work one day. Continuing to use enemas will create a disgruntled employee who may never want to work for you again. The spinal nerve that relates to the intestines will also be relieved of its duties, and will not get a good letter of recommendation from its employer!

Dr. Palmer, the founding father of chiropractic, wrote about the "one question [that] was always uppermost in my mind in my search for the cause of disease. I desired to know why one person was ailing and why his associate, eating at the same table, working in the same shop, at the same bench, was not." This line of thought is the foundation for the major subluxation principle: Everybody is the same, and everybody is different. We have different weaknesses. An aspirin may work on one person's headache and not on another's. One man can throw a baseball at ninety miles per hour; another can't. Some pack-a-day cigarette smokers get cancer; some two-packers don't. This answer lies in their weaknesses. One factor accounting for weakness is the subluxation.

As mentioned earlier, a subluxation may occur through chemical means. A drug puts a strain on the system, and the vertebral segment responds by causing a "kink in the hose," a pinching of the spinal nerve. Other spinal weaknesses are acquired through physical trauma. Still others are caused—or, more precisely, aggravated—by mental stress. You're pressured by a deadline, so you get a headache, an upset stomach, or begin to hyperventilate. This is why lifelong chiropractic is necessary, not just for pain, but to remove the subluxation before it can fester into a crisis. This is known as maintenance care, or preventive medicine.

The subluxation is not just a concept; it's quite tangible. You can see it during laboratory dissections. Studies have shown that many people who die from heart attacks display subluxations relating to the heart area. The same is true for individuals who die of stomach cancer, kidney failure, and liver disease. A subluxation crowds and adversely affects the contents of the intervertebral foramen, or IVF (see Chapter 3). The IVF, an opening created by two adjacent vertebrae, encloses several important soft-tissue structures, including the spinal nerve, lymphatic vessels, spinal arteries, meninges (the spinal-cord cover), and spinal fluid. (Spinal fluid exists in such delicate balance that removal of even a single drop is enough to cause headaches and convulsions.)

Studies have shown that pressure on the IVF causes its contents to atrophy, that is, to become less vital. If the subluxation isn't corrected, the same health problems will return. The same spot on the back will hurt. The same old leg pain will flare up. The same stomach problems will continue to make your life miserable. Fortunately, most of our cells (except for nerve cells) are eventually replenished with new cells. Eventually, you get a whole new stomach, heart, liver, and so on. Some cells, as in the blood and skin, replenish themselves very quickly—every 10 to 30 hours. Other cells, such as in the liver, may have a lifespan of 500 days.[1, 2]

1  Reader's Digest. *The ABC's of the Human Body: A Family Answer Book.* The Reader's Digest Association, Inc., 1987; pp. 26-27.

2  Whitfield, Philip. *The Human Body Explained.* Henry Holt & Company, Inc., 1995; pp. 138-139.

So, then, if we are constantly regenerating our inventory, why does heart disease continue or worsen over five or ten years? The answer is faulty cell programming. If you neglect to tune a piano string, it will play out of tune each time you press the key. If you don't "tune" your spinal nerves, they will continue to give faulty or sick commands, which will, in turn, perpetuate the impairment of organs.

Modern chiropractors do not claim to cure everything. The old ones didn't either. Neither do chiropractors contend that the subluxation is the only cause of disease, or that fixing subluxations will cure all diseases. The basic idea of chiropractic is to remove irritating factors from the body, and let it heal itself. Give the natural recuperative powers of your body a chance. You'll be amazed at how much healing your body can accomplish when you don't punish it with an unhealthy lifestyle.

## Primary Causes of Canine Subluxations

The subluxation theory applies to all vertebrates, including dogs. Most dogs have stress-related subluxations stemming from the behavior of their demanding owners.

The improper use of collars is the number one cause of cervical (neck) subluxations in dogs. Of all the places to put undue stress, the cervical region, especially the upper two cervical vertebrae, is the most harmful. It is at this point that the body meets the brain. All nerve-signal transmissions must pass through the brain stem on their way to the brain for the processing of information. An upper cervical blockage, or subluxation, renders other spinal adjustments useless. The upper spine is so important that B.J. Palmer at one time taught upper-cervical technique and nothing else.

While almost all dog owners use some type of collar on their pet, the average dog owner merely guesses about what kind to use—usually the one that's on sale, or the one the store has in stock. The collar should fit the dog's job, breed, and height, as well as the dog's size in relation to the owner. A study of 400 show dogs in Sweden reported that about 90 percent of all upper-cervical subluxations were the direct result of improper training corrections by dog handlers and owners jerking on leashes and collars.

There are four major types of dog collars: the *flat collar*, the *choke collar*, the *prong collar*, and the *harness* (Fig. 2-1). The flat collar is the most common type, and can be dangerous if misused. It simply acts as an attachment for the leash so the dog won't get loose during daily walks. It should not be used for obedience training, since it does not guide the dog in a specific direction when yanked. A frustrated owner who has difficulty controlling his pet will pull the dog in such a manner as to cause tremendous cervical muscle tightening, thus producing subluxations. This is one of the reasons why canine cervical subluxations are epidemic. The family who owns the dog may consist of four or more people, all of whom who are yanking the dog's neck in a different manner, depending on the individual's strength, height, and frustration level.

The second type of collar is the choke collar. While this collar successfully restrains the dog and is recommended by dog trainers, there is theoretically no limit on how much this collar will choke. If a dog is particularly excited, it can liter-

flat collar

choke collar

prong collar

harness

Fig. 2-1.
Types of collars.

ally choke itself into a coma. An improperly trained dog is especially vulnerable.

The third type is the prong collar. This device, with its circular ring of spikes on the inner surface of the collar, looks menacing, but most of the literature suggests that this is the most effective and least dangerous of restraining collars. The prong collar distributes the pressure evenly around the neck, and requires only a small amount of force. It also has the advantage of being self-limiting, unlike the choke collar. Some trainers liken the prong collar to "power steering" where even the slightest touch will produce the desired result. Incidence of canine upper cervical subluxations is far less with the prong collar. Nevertheless, prong collars are beset by controversy and are banned in AKC (American Kennel Club) competitions.

The fourth type is the harness, commonly used to restrain small dogs. Although harnesses are normally thought of as being easier on the neck, they can be hard on the front half of the body, including the chest and forelegs. Harnesses have little training value.

Some obedience schools insist that the dog walk to the left of the owner during training. Furthermore, the dog is instructed to look at the owner's belt, thus causing the animal to constantly crane its head to the right. This causes major upper-cervical subluxations and is just one example of how obedience schools sacrifice a dog's health for the sake of good looks. (How many people make the same kinds of sacrifices?)

Clearly, then, owner frustration and the lack of dog-training knowledge are the primary causes of canine cervical subluxations. Mismatching dog to owner is another cause. A petite person should have a small dog, and so on. This is as important for the health of the owner as it is for the dog's.

Other causes of canine subluxations include:

1. **Obesity.** Obesity exerts pressure on the spine, which in turn causes weak muscles and ligaments. Not only does excess fat cause subluxations, it reduces the chance that an adjustment will hold.

2. **Improper bedding.** Dogs should get used to one comfortable place to sleep, preferably a flat surface with moderately firm padding, like a wrestling mat. Studies have shown that dogs need support when they sleep, just as people do.

3. **Harmful training practices.** Dog owners are emotionally attached to their animals, and therefore should not train them themselves. (If you are frustrated, your dog will become equally frustrated.) But while professional trainers will get your dog to behave, their methods will often result in neck subluxations. As mentioned, some training methods have the dog look to its right and up at the owner or trainer. This causes unilateral muscle spasms and a sore neck. Horses have mid-back subluxations for almost the same reason, since riders always climb onto the horse from its left side.

4. **Dangerous play practices.** Dogs are loyal and will do anything for their owners. If your dog appears to be in pain after a playing session, review your activities and delete the ones that appeared most demanding.

5. **Breed limitations.** A bulldog, for instance, does not

have the same leg structure as a greyhound, so don't expect it to run as fast or as long.

6. **Leash length.** Holding a dog too close with a short leash will limit the dog's stride and cause chronic postural stress.

7. **Psychological considerations.** Scolding for things that come naturally, like barking at a rabbit or chasing a cat, confuses the dog and can lead to stress and muscle tension.

8. **Caged dogs.** Where there is no room to move around, there is no way to relieve muscular stress. "Confinement will cause misalignment" is a good motto to remember.

9. **Fleas.** Fleas and mites cause subluxations, because the dog is always scratching his itches in awkward positions.

While you can't monitor your dog's every move, you can check for subluxations. Because so many different things cause subluxations, check your dog often. You'll be saving him a lot of pain.

# CHAPTER 3

# BONES, JOINTS,
# MUSCLES, AND NERVES

Most people equate chiropractors with bones. Some say they're visiting their chiropractor this week to "have their bones cracked." Nothing could be further from the truth. Orthopedic surgeons, not chiropractors, treat bones. Chiropractors do, however, make use of bones as levers to affect joints, muscles, and nerves. Chiropractors manipulate various parts of the body, especially the spine, to improve the body's overall performance and mobility.

The methods used to manipulate the body depend largely on the size and the location of a bone. Longer bones, such as those of the arms and legs, are easier to manipulate because their length makes them more accessible. You can grasp a long bone with your hands. Smaller bones, such as the bones of the spine (vertebrae), cannot be gripped like long bones; therefore, they must be pushed or pulled with the fingers.

The canine skeleton is composed of about 319 separate bones. (The number varies slightly because the number of tail bones differs from breed to breed.) In addition to giving the body its structure, bones store minerals, produce blood cells, and provide the surfaces to which muscles attach.

The main functional difference between the human and the canine skeleton is that people walk upright on the soles of their feet and carry most of their weight on their hips. Dogs walk on their toes and on all fours, carrying more than half their weight on their front limbs and shoulders.

## BACK BONES

The practice of chiropractic centers around manipulating the back bones (vertebrae). Between each back bone joint there is an important nerve called a *spinal nerve*. The spinal nerve exits through a small opening formed by two adjacent vertebrae. This opening is called the *intervertebral foramen*, or IVF (Fig. 3-1). Taut back muscles can squeeze and narrow these openings, putting pressure on the spinal nerves. The spinal nerves branch out to all of the organs in the body. If a nerve is squeezed or

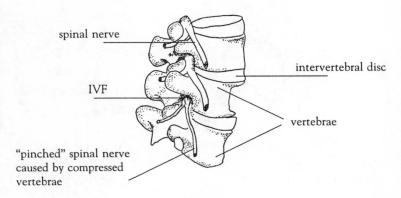

Fig. 3-1.
Intervertebral Foramen, or IVF. (*Human example.*)

pinched off at the IVF, the signals it sends to the organs are impaired.

Aside from the spinal nerves, the IVFs contain other important structures, such as spinal arteries, vertebral veins, lymphatic vessels, and part of the covering of the spinal cord (meninges). This opening is so vital to overall good health that many types of back surgeries performed by orthopedic surgeons involve the IVF. A *laminectomy*, for example, is a surgical procedure that helps create a larger IVF by removing some bone tissue so the corresponding spinal nerve has more space, and also to allow the compressed spinal cord to bulge upward (dorsally). Likewise, removing part of a spinal disc (discectomy) also helps open up the IVF.

A dog's back is divided into three sections: the *neck* (seven cervical vertebrae), the *mid-back* (thirteen thoracic or dorsal vertebrae), and the *low back* (seven lumbar vertebrae). These

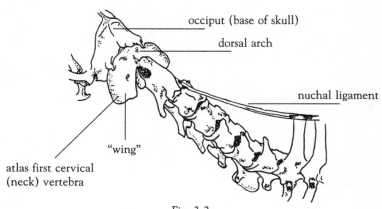

Fig. 3-2.
Dog's neck bones (*dorsal view—back of dog's neck*).

sections have definite starting and stopping points.

The neck starts directly underneath the base of the skull. The top neck bone, the large, ring-shaped *atlas*, holds up the head (Fig. 3-2). This bone can easily be felt at both sides of your dog's neck by placing your fingers off to the side of the head and slightly down from the ears (Fig. 3-3). Most of the other neck bones can be felt by carefully palpating the sides of your dog's neck until you reach the shoulder area (Fig. 3-4).

As you come to the end of the neck, you will feel more pronounced bumps sticking out at the center line of the back. These bumps are called *spinous processes* (a.k.a. *dorsal processes*), commonly referred to as "spines" (Fig. 3-5). The spines run in a line down the back, and are of varied lengths. Place your fingers on the center of your dog's neck and feel the bumps. Then firmly move your fingers down his entire back, all the way down to his tail (Fig. 3-6). You will feel spines all the way down.

Some, you'll notice, are easier to find than others. The spines in the upper and middle part of the neck are very short and cannot readily be felt—with the exception of the second neck bone, or *axis*, the spine of which can easily be felt by touching a spot about an inch below the base of the skull of an average-size dog (Fig. 3-7).

The mid-back bones feel more rigid than the neck bones when you push into the spines, because the sides of the mid-back bones are attached to ribs. You can feel rib bumps next to each side of the spines. Place your fingers towards the end of the mid-back. It feels as though one of the bones is missing. It's not. The eleventh thoracic vertebra is slightly recessed in the

Feeling the atlas
(*slightly higher than fingers show*)

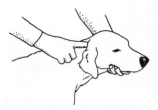

Actual site of atlas

Feeling atlas wings with
your index fingers

Feeling the atlas with your
index finger and thumb

Fig. 3-3.
The atlas.

Fig. 3-4.
Feeling the sides of the neck.

Fig. 3-5.
Feeling the "spines"
(*upper back*).

Fig. 3-6.
Feeling the "spines"
(*mid to lower back*).

Touching the second
neck bone (axis)

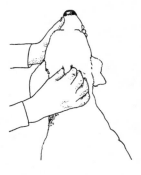

"Pinching' the second
neck bone

Fig. 3-7.
The axis (second neck bone).

back and therefore feels like a depression.

The spines of the low back feel much like those of the mid-back, only there are no ribs to make the low back feel rigid.

## Joints

Study Fig. 3-8 while feeling your dog's bones to find out where they start and end, and where they connect to each other. A bone would have no function if it didn't somehow connect to another bone.

Joints are where two or more bones meet and are held together by tough fibrous tissue called *ligament*. An injured ligament is called a "sprain," as opposed to a "strain," which is an injured *tendon*. A tendon is inelastic fibrous tissue that con-

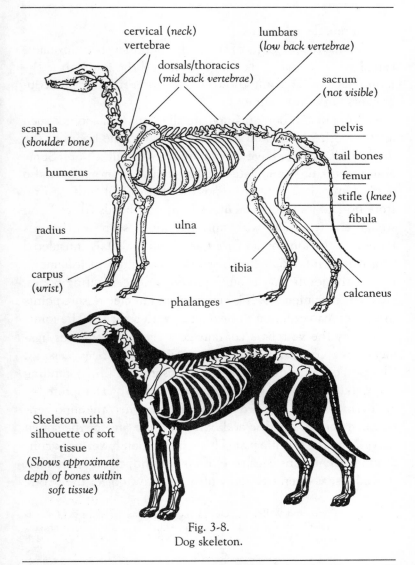

Fig. 3-8.
Dog skeleton.

Labels (clockwise from top):
cervical (*neck*) vertebrae
lumbars (*low back vertebrae*)
dorsals/thoracics (*mid back vertebrae*)
sacrum (*not visible*)
scapula (*shoulder bone*)
pelvis
humerus
tail bones
femur
stifle (*knee*)
fibula
radius
ulna
carpus (*wrist*)
tibia
phalanges
calcaneus

Skeleton with a silhouette of soft tissue (*Shows approximate depth of bones within soft tissue*) nects a muscle to a bone.

The moveable joints of the body contain a slick substance called *synovial fluid*. This fluid is what oils the joints. It is the most effective lubricant known to exist on earth, synthetic lubricants notwithstanding.[1]

Chiropractors don't manipulate all joints. Some joints, such as the tooth sockets and the joints between the bones of the skull, don't move or have very limited movement. (**Note:** Some chiropractors *do* manipulate the skull joints.) Chiropractors also don't manipulate joints to reposition bones, but rather to restore normal joint movement. A joint that bends (flexes) and straightens (extends) with minimal effort, such as the ones formed by the long bones (front and hind limbs), is considered "normal." Joints riddled with arthritis, a permanent inflammation of the joints that is often present in degenerating bones, are hard to manipulate. It is better to use muscle pressure points instead of manipulation to treat a dog with arthritis. The joints formed by the vertebrae contain *discs* (Fig. 3-9), fibrous ligaments that contain a fluid center called the *nucleus pulposus*. The purpose of a disc is for shock absorption while standing and walking. You may know of someone who's had a ruptured—or "herniated," or "slipped"—disc. This is when the fluid center bursts out of the disc and oozes into the area of the spinal nerves, causing horrific pain. This is a common lower-back condition with humans because of their upright posture. A human slipped disc is often caused by lifting a heavy object the wrong

[1] Warwick, Roger, and Williams, Peter L. *Gray's Anatomy, 35th British Edition.* W.B. Saunders Company, 1973; p. 396 (note their references listed on column 2, paragraph 1).

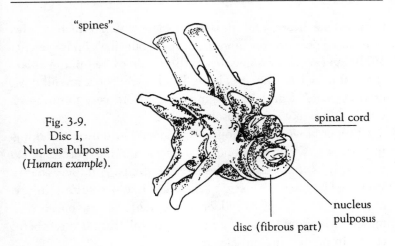

Fig. 3-9.
Disc I,
Nucleus Pulposus
(*Human example*).

"spines"

spinal cord

nucleus
pulposus

disc (fibrous part)

way, and usually shows up between the two lowest back bones (lumbars). However, a dog walks on all four legs with its spine in a horizontal position, and is therefore not as prone to herniated discs in the low back (though some breeds are more predisposed to herniated discs than others, e.g., Dachshunds). This explains why dogs' discs are proportionately thinner than ours; they don't need to absorb as much shock.

## MUSCLES

*Muscles* are soft fibrous tissues that contract and produce body movements when energized by nerve impulses. They also give the body bulk and shape, and can become knotted in response to sudden movements.

There are three types of muscles in the body: *smooth muscles*, found in blood vessels and hollow organs; *cardiac muscles*, found only in the heart; and *skeletal muscles*, which attach to the bones and account for more than half your dog's body weight. Whenever we discuss muscles in this book, we're talking about skeletal muscles. The legs, back, head, and thorax are all covered by skeletal muscles ranging in size from very minute eye muscles to bulky rump muscles.

Proper movement of joints is produced by muscles working in harmony. When your body is in motion, some muscles relax while others contract. Muscles have elasticity. A muscle that is stretched before an athletic event is less likely to sustain injury because it can adapt to sudden movements better than a stiff muscle. Massaging your dog before you walk him is often beneficial in preventing muscle spasms.

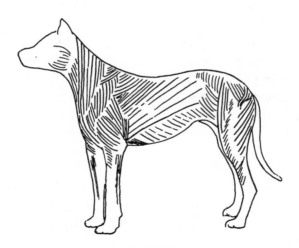

Fig. 3-10.
Muscles—note the striations.
(*Muscle names omitted.*)

Since all the bones you'll feel on your dog have muscles, study the muscle diagrams carefully (Fig. 3-10). This will give you a good idea of muscle size and location. As you're studying the diagrams, note also the direction ("striations") of the muscle fibers. Knowing the direction of the fibers is important when applying pressure-point or massage methods. If you want to "clean out" a muscle and help it heal after an injury, massage against the grain of the muscle fibers for about two minutes per muscle knot, up to five treatments per week. This is called Transverse Friction Massage (TFM). An injured muscle needs a constant flow of blood and lymph in order to rebuild itself, and TFM helps the muscle attain this.

When a muscle feels thick and fleshy, you are probably touching the center ("belly") of the muscle. This is the site of most muscle knots and trigger points. As you'll learn in the "Methods" chapters, you can accomplish most pain treatments by simply pressing your finger into a muscle knot.

When feeling for a particular muscle on your dog, feel for it in all postures—that is, standing, sitting, relaxed, flexed, or extended—and in as many actions as possible. An injured or spastic muscle will restrict movement in several postures.

## NERVES

Nerves are everywhere on the body. (Try to find a place on your body that doesn't hurt when you stick a pin into it.) They are what energize your muscles and organs.

The nervous system is divided into two parts: the *central nervous system*, which includes your brain and spinal cord, and

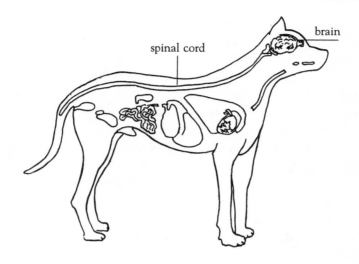

Fig. 3-11.
Nervous system (*brain and cord*).

the *peripheral nervous system*, which includes everything else (Fig. 3-11). The spinal nerves are part of the peripheral nervous system, and the spine is the area most often treated by chiropractors for pinched nerves (Fig. 3-12).

There is frequently a confusion of terms relating to the back, especially of the differences between the *spinal cord*, the *spinal column*, and *spinal nerves*. The spinal cord is nerve tissue protected within the spinal column (back bones or vertebrae), much as the brain is protected by the skull. Spinal nerves are long nerves that originate in the spinal cord and pass through openings in the spinal column, making their

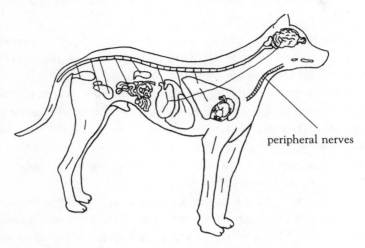

Fig. 3-12.
Nerves go everywhere, including the organs.

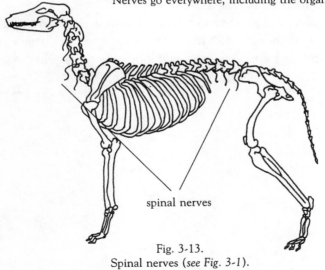

Fig. 3-13.
Spinal nerves (*see* Fig. 3-1).

way to the rest of the body (Fig. 3-13).

The peripheral nervous system also contains those nerves over which you have little or no control, such as the nerves that control your breathing while you sleep.

This is particularly important because your dog may not show any signs of distress from this part of the nervous system (called the "autonomic nervous system"), while all the time he may be experiencing the effects of a pinched nerve in his back. This is why you must always check your dog's spine for subluxations. Stop problems before they happen.

In general, the spinal nerves located at the upper part of your dog's back control the front legs. The low-back spinal nerves control his rear legs. His mid-back spinal nerves control surrounding muscles. Almost the entire range of spinal nerves regulates internal organs in some way (see Chapter 14).

You can't feel pinched nerves, only signs of pinched nerves, such as misaligned bones and tight muscles. Your dog knows for sure where he hurts. And now you'll be able to help him.

# CHAPTER 4

# CONTRAINDICATIONS

Contraindications are reasons why you shouldn't use chiropractic manipulation on your dog. It may be that manipulation would be harmful if applied, or manipulation may simply be the wrong treatment for the condition and serve only to delay the use of appropriate therapies.

1. **Fractures**. Never adjust a bone that has an unhealed fracture, or a bone near such a fracture.
2. **Recent trauma**. A fall, an auto accident, a fight with another dog—all are reasons to have your dog checked by a veterinarian. Even if you only suspect that your dog's back pain is due to an injury, do not adjust.
3. **Vicious or unpredictable dog.** No matter how badly the dog needs to be adjusted, do not attempt manipulation when you are in danger.
4. **Vascular conditions (Rare).** Only a veterinarian can determine this. A buildup of plaque in the vertebral arteries would contraindicate spinal manipulation, especially of the neck.
5. **Tumors**. The possibility of causing a fracture by ren-

dering an adjustment is increased in the cancer patient, especially if the bone itself is malignant.

6. **Bone infections**. While these are rare, they still exist and should be ruled out by a veterinary medical examination. Some signs of active bone infections are tissue atrophy, increased warmth, and edema (swelling). Sometimes a soft-tissue mass will be present that lacks roundness and will change shape under pressure.

7. **Nerve damage**. The sensation over these areas is usually decreased; therefore, the degree of susceptibility to injury cannot be adequately assessed.

8. **Old surgical scars**, especially on or near a joint. These are signs that the dog has had something wrong with it. Find out what it was before you adjust.

9. **Profuse joint swelling**. Large areas of increased heat and excess fluid are signs of a serious medical condition.

10. **Arthritis**. This doesn't always apply to all dogs with arthritis; it refers primarily to severe cases. Arthritic dogs cannot be easily adjusted, and the practitioner may be tempted to use unacceptable force to perform the adjustment. This is where soft-tissue techniques are useful.

11. **Skin lesions**. Adjusting over a lesion can aggravate the site and cause infections.

12. **Recent surgery**. This includes dogs who have just been spayed or neutered.

13. **Prostheses**. This caution applies to adjustment of the extremities. You can still do a vertebral adjustment,

just be extra careful during the stabilization phase of the treatment. A dog with a prosthesis can't effectively support itself during a "standing" procedure. This often depends on the effectiveness of the replacement limb.

14. **Medications**. Pain-killers and anti-inflammatory drugs, such as phenylbutazone, can often mask symptoms—even though chiropractic care may help reduce the need for such medications. Side effects of medications (as well as some food supplements) may present themselves as subluxations, i.e., increased or decreased muscle tone over the spine.

15. **Herniated, or "slipped," disc**. Do not adjust at the site of the herniation; rather, work on the surrounding subluxations.

# CHAPTER 5

# ADJUSTING SKILLS

Just as a pianist has to know how hard to press the key to create the right sound, the canine adjuster should develop certain sensitivities in their hands. There are two physical requirements for administering an adjustment: manual dexterity and muscular coordination.

## MANUAL DEXTERITY

Traditional chiropractic moves rely on the mind and hand acting as one without hesitation. The type of movement your hands have to make during the adjustment is akin to your wrist action when cracking a whip, or to *Peanuts'* Linus "nailing" a fly out of the air with one quick snap of his blanket. It's speed, not force, that gets the job done safely. Because the reader of this book won't be doing a lot of "cracking" moves, he or she should focus on developing a keen sense of touch and tactile depth perception. Most of the following methods involve pushing, without having to actually deliver a thrust into a bone or joint.

## Exercises to Improve Finger and Hand Skills

1. **Palpation exercise.** This will help to develop your sense of touch. Place a hair under a piece of notebook paper and see if you can feel the hair underneath. Then put the hair under two pieces of paper, and so on, until you're no longer able to feel the hair. If you can still feel the hair underneath five sheets of paper, you're above average.

2. **Testing finger depth perception.** Take a two-inch thick piece of Styrofoam, hold it down with one hand for stabilization, and place your other thumb on the Styrofoam's surface, keeping your wrist straight. This will be your adjusting hand.

   Situate yourself above the Styrofoam with the elbow of your adjusting arm slightly bent. Now deliver a sudden impulse into the Styrofoam. Your thumb should not make a dent deeper than a quarter inch, even with a full and sudden thrust.

3. **Finger dexterity test.** With the palm of your hand on a table and your fingers slightly spread, place a quarter underneath the tip of your pinky. Then, without moving your pinky, slide your ring finger next to your pinky and pull the coin away, positioning it under your ring finger. Repeat this procedure for all your fingers, including your thumb. Then reverse the direction of the fingers. Do this until you can pass the coin from one side of your hand to the next in about five seconds.

# Muscular Coordination

At the time of the thrust, your muscles must move in a clean, flawless motion. Your goal is to achieve bull's-eye accuracy.

## Exercises to Improve Muscular Coordination

1. Practice driving a two-inch screw into a piece of wood without having to reinsert the screwdriver head.
2. Have someone throw three balls at you, one at a time in rapid succession. Catch and drop each ball with the same hand.
3. Toss two coins in the air and, with two separate grabs, catch them both.

# General Advice

1. Never push into your dog's mid-back without supporting his belly or chest area with your other hand. A human who gets adjusted can lie on his belly because his rib cage can absorb a light to moderate thrust coming from their back. A dog, however, has a much more vulnerable rib cage configuration and cannot absorb a downward thrust if he is forced to lie sprawled out on his belly.
2. For thrusting moves that deliver a sudden impulse into a joint, the force behind the thrust originates from the contraction of your triceps and pectorals (Fig. 5-1).
3. For a "Set and Hold" adjustment, your hands remain

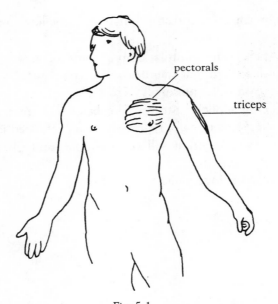

Fig. 5-1.
Muscles used for contraction when performing
a "quick reflex" impulse during the adjustment.

at the end of the thrusting position for a few moments
to prevent a recoil of the vertebra. This only applies
after you've delivered a sudden impulse into a joint.

4. You do not always hear an audible sound or "pop" during the adjustment. Sometimes you will simply feel
the vertebrae slide into place.

5. If you want to adjust just one bone, you must contact
only that bone. Contacting two bones divides the energy of your thrust in half.

6. The adjusting thrust is a high-velocity, low-amplitude (force) maneuver.
7. When pushing into a "spine," joint, or muscle, never push so hard that your dog yelps. The phrase "No pain, no gain" does not apply here.
8. Do not apply heat to your dog before the treatment. If your dog is in pain, he may have an inflamed joint or joint swelling that will become worse under heat.
9. Cut your nails.
10. Cut your dog's nails.

# CHAPTER 6

# RULES FOR HANDLING AND SAFETY

These next couple of pages will instruct you on proper canine handling procedures, both before and after examination and adjustment. The key word here is **safety**, for both you and your dog. *If ever a situation arises that jeopardizes your own safety or that of the dog, stop your treatment procedures.* Remember, a dog in pain is likely to be less than congenial—so be patient with your patient!

**RULE 1.** At times, you should enlist the cooperation of another person to assist you with the adjustment. The first contact with the dog is made by you, the owner. Then—gradually, playfully—the dog may be handled by your assistant.

**RULE 2.** Always work in an enclosed area—more accurately, a place from which the dog cannot escape into danger. You don't want your patient bolting into the street!

**RULE 3.** Use a muzzle! Be wary of the dog whose owner says, "Duke? No, he doesn't bite!" I assure you, Duke does bite, and *will* bite, if not properly muzzled. The muzzle has to be tight enough so the dog cannot open its mouth even slightly. If the dog can open its mouth at all, it can bite!

You can buy a muzzle from a pet shop or make your own restraint. Here's how. With the aid of another person holding the dog firmly from behind, wrap a strip of gauze, a nylon stocking, or a length of soft, thin rope (such as a clothesline) tightly around the dog's muzzle (Fig. 6-1). Bring both free ends of the rope up around the neck behind the ears and tie them off at the back of the head. This will not interfere with your dog's breathing during the brief adjustment.

It is also acceptable to use the Dixie-cup style, or enclosed, muzzle, which allows the dog to lick and pant without feeling restricted. Still, it is my opinion that you should simply go out and buy a tight-fitting muzzle. They work better.

**RULE 4.** Heed the dog's warning. A well-cared-for dog will usually give you a few warning growls, signaling that it's uncomfortable with you or that you've just touched a sensitive spot. When this happens, withdraw your hands and start again at an area removed from the pain.

**RULE 5.** Handle the dog on a carpeted or other sure-footed surface. This is more of a suggestion than a rule, as there are two lines of thought regarding the best surface. A veterinarian's examination table is usually slippery; some vets like this because the slippery surface disconcerts the dog, making it afraid to move. On the other hand, the chiropractic adjusting force may cause the dog to lose its balance on a slippery surface.

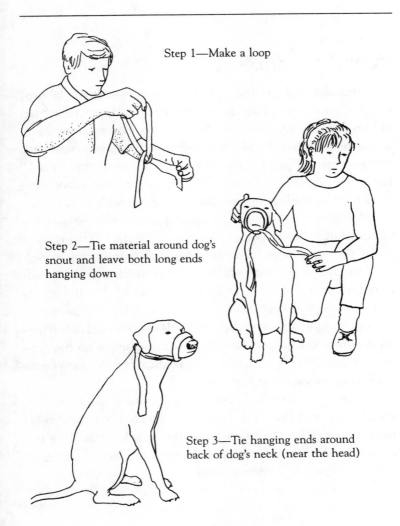

Step 1—Make a loop

Step 2—Tie material around dog's snout and leave both long ends hanging down

Step 3—Tie hanging ends around back of dog's neck (near the head)

Fig. 6-1.
Steps for making a muzzle.

# A Note on Sedatives

An often-debated question is whether sedatives should be used to relax an animal before an adjustment. Chiropractic purists say no to sedatives. For one thing, chiropractors cannot prescribe medications. For another, sedatives are inconsistent with chiropractic philosophy. In order for an adjustment to "hold," the patient must go into it with good muscle tone. Also, sedatives tend to mask symptoms such as tight muscles.

However, there is a group of chiropractors who espouse the use of Manipulation Under Anesthesia (MUA). This is done under the supervision of an anesthesiologist in a hospital setting on human patients who are in too much pain to be adjusted normally. There is research to support MUA, and it may be the wave of the future.

But in most settings where animals are adjusted, anesthetics are impractical. Still, licensed veterinarians who have already sedated their patients for other medical reasons may choose to do their adjusting at that time.

Once upon a time, I had the opportunity to perform an adjustment on a lion. The beast had already been sedated for the purpose of having its toenails trimmed. Had the lion not been sedated, I would not have entered the cage—unless, of course, I myself had been sedated!

# Biting and Least Biting Breeds

This next bit of information should be filed in a "for what it's worth" section. I found an entry in a book titled *The Book Of Lists*[1] which said: "This list was so popular in the People's Almanac that we thought we would run it again for those who may have missed it. After a 27-year study of the canine population of New York, N.Y., Dr. Robert Oleson of the U.S. Public Health Service came up with the nine bitingest (sic) dogs. He found that the time of year in which you will most likely be bitten is not July or August, the 'dog days,' but the middle of June." And the dogs most likely to do it, ranked in order of their biting averages, are:

1. German police dog
2. Chow
3. Poodle
4. Italian bulldog
5. Fox terrier
6. Crossed chow
7. Airedale terrier
8. Pekingese
9. Crossed German police dog

This book notes that Dobermans didn't make the list and neither did mongrels.

[1] Wallechinsky, David; Wallace, Irving; and Wallace, Amy. *The Book Of Lists*; Wiliam Morrow And Company, Inc., 1977.

The breeds of dogs that bite the *least* are:

1. Golden retriever
2. Labrador retriever
3. Shetland sheepdog
4. Old English sheepdog
5. Welsh terrier
6. Yorkshire terrier
7. Beagle
8. Dalmatian
9. Pointer

My advice is to be wary of *all* dogs. You will find that some dogs won't cooperate during the examination or treatment. Approach each dog as if you expect it to give you trouble.

# CHAPTER 7

# HOW DO YOU KNOW WHERE A DOG HURTS? (LOCATING CANINE SUBLUXATIONS)

The title of this chapter is the question most frequently asked of canine chiropractors. A variation would be "How do you know when your dog needs chiropractic care?" The first question will be answered in this chapter. The answers to the second question can be summed up in one sentence: Your dog needs chiropractic care when a subluxation (i.e., misaligned vertebra that pinches a nerve) exists. Vertebral subluxations, as you'll discover, have several predictable and palpable features: tight and tender muscles flanking the "spines," restricted movement as your fingers press into a vertebral joint, and increased heat over the tight muscles. These, along with the lameness signs, should help you determine if your dog is subluxated.

There are several factors that determine how your dog feels. Recent injuries, age, sex, current medications, and weight are some of the things to consider while inspecting your dog for signs of pain and subluxation. Older dogs, for example, will almost always feel stiff due to arthritis. Older male dogs may also have low-back pain due to prostate disease. Female dogs often have back pain after giving birth. Active dogs, such as greyhounds, are prone to athletic injuries such as sprains and ligament tears. And the effects on your dog of anti-inflammatory drugs, analgesics, or other medications can cloud your own observations altogether.

As a human being, you are equipped with all the tools you'll need to find out where your dog hurts. Your senses, especially sight and touch, are your guide. When examining your dog, a good motto to follow is "Feel what you see, and see what you feel." Observation is your first contact with your dog.

Most muscular problems and areas of subluxation are first noticed when your dog is in motion. Watch him walk, run, jump, or chase something. Is he getting easily from point A to point B? Can he adapt to changing terrain without difficulty? If your answers are "no," then ask yourself why. Why can't your dog move about as before? Is it due to his neck, legs, or back?

To find the answers to such questions, study the list below. Pay particular attention to your dog's legs during walking, running, and standing. The following signs of trouble will train your eye to look for the "red flags" of pain, especially by observing the limbs. Most vertebral subluxations have three things in common: taut and tender muscle fibers that can be felt next to the "spines," increased heat at these tender muscle areas, and decreased vertebral joint motion. However, several "lameness" signs can also be clues to finding subluxations.

## Twelve Signs of Trouble

1. If the hind limbs get crossed during walking, this could

indicate a painful low back. Feel your dog's low back for tight muscles.

2. If your dog weaves during walking or running, this usually indicates a problem with one of his elbows. This is because the front legs act as "rudders," while the hind legs are used more for propulsion. If you suspect a bad elbow, sit next to your dog and gently squeeze the suspect elbow. Does it feel spongy? If so, there may be water present (edema), which is a sign of an injury for which prompt medical help should be sought.

3. If your dog is limping, the limb that moves first (leads) during walking is the one that hurts.

4. Constantly shifting legs while standing on all fours indicates pain, but not necessarily in the legs. Notice which legs shift. If the front legs shift, then feel for tight neck and shoulder muscles. If the hind legs shift, then feel for tight low-back muscles.

5. While standing, your dog's body weight should be equally distributed on all fours; if it is not, feel the favored side for excessive muscle tightness or joint swelling.

6. Front-leg pain should be suspected when your dog takes a short step on one leg (the one that hurts) as he beings to walk, then reaches with the other leg.

7. On large-breed dogs, the head will come up as the bad leg reaches the ground.

8. Your dog is in pain when three of his legs act as a supporting tripod for the fourth leg.

9. The painful limb is usually the one that's bent while standing.

10. While standing on all fours, the painful leg's paw appears smaller than the opposite paw, since less pressure is put on the painful one.
11. A dog will often lie on his painful side. This supports the painful limb, much as a sling supports a sore shoulder.
12. With your dog standing on all fours, lift each of his legs, one at a time. The one that lifts off the floor easiest is the painful limb, because he's avoiding putting pressure on it.

Once you have determined which limb is in pain, then look for signs of neck and back pain. The majority of subluxations are found at the transition areas of the spine, that is, where the neck begins (at the base of the skull), where the neck ends and the mid-back begins (shoulder area), where the mid-back ends and the low back (lumbar region) begins, and where the lumbars end (at the sacrum).

## CHECKING FOR NECK PAIN & SUBLUXATIONS

An unusual head position is a sure sign of neck pain. A dog's head that remains tilted for more than fifteen seconds without change means his neck muscles are in spasm. The side of the spasm is often the side of the head tilt, because the dog will tilt his head towards the most comfortable position, stretching the side with less pain.

### A Quick Neck Test

Sit next to your dog and place one hand under his chin while

Fig. 7-1.

Fig. 7-2.
Testing the "yes" joint (*the joint between the base of the skull and the atlas, or first neck bone*).

Fig. 7-3.

Fig. 7-4.
Testing the "no" joint (*the joint between the first and second neck bones*).

placing your other hand behind his neck (Fig. 7-1). Gently push his neck backwards as far as it will go (Fig. 7-2) while feeling the neck muscles. Notice whether you can push your dog's neck backwards all in one motion, or if there are any "stops" along the way. The sides of the neck can be tested in a similar manner, by laterally flexing the dog's neck over your finger (Fig. 7-3). "Stops" indicate pain or a frozen neck joint. The upper-neck bones allow the dog to move his head in a "yes" motion and a "no" motion. Feel the back of your dog's neck and guide his head in these two motions (Fig. 7-4). The neck should be able to move in both directions without hesitation. The "yes" motion is felt at the joint between the first neck bone (atlas) and the base of the skull; the "no" motion is felt at the joint created by the atlas and the second neck bone (axis). **Important note:** Congenital atlanto-axial joint (first and second neck bone, respectively) subluxations in toy breeds can be dangerous to manipulate, especially in puppies.

## CHECKING FOR MID~BACK PAIN & SUBLUXATIONS

The two major signs of mid-back pain are shallow breathing and random hard muscle sites. If you notice your dog breathing in short, quick breaths after strenuous activity, it may be that he can't adequately expand his rib cage. This can be a sign of mid-back pain.

Once you suspect your dog has mid-back pain, feel his thoracic vertebrae by placing your middle or index finger on his first mid-back vertebra (Fig. 7-5). Then feel all of the mid-back bones by scanning them in one motion until you have reached

Fig. 7-5.
Feeling the first mid-back
(thoracic) vertebra.

Fig. 7-6.
Visually scanning the placement of small
pieces of tape, placed on each mid-back spine,
helps determine off-center vertebrae.

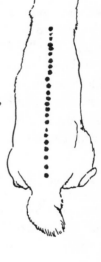

Fig. 7-7.
Feeling the low-back
(lumbar) spines.

the last one (number thirteen, about six inches up from the root of the tail, depending on the size of your dog). Next, go back to the first thoracic and feel each individual bone. It is sometimes helpful to place a small, round piece of tape or paper stickers over each bump ("spine") (Fig. 7-6). This enables you to see which bones are off-center in one glance, and will help you determine which ones to adjust.

Once you have located an off-center spine, feel the muscles surrounding it. If the bone is off-center and has a tight muscle, you've found the bone that needs to be treated.

## CHECKING FOR LOW~BACK PAIN & SUBLUXATIONS

The low-back bones (lumbar vertebrae) are felt in the same line as the mid-back bones. The low-back bones do not have ribs attached to them as do the mid-back bones; therefore, the lower back is more flexible.

Feel the seven "spines" of the low-back bones, starting with the first to the last (about two inches above the base of the tail) (Fig. 7-7). Again, place small pieces of tape over each spine to see if any of them are off-center. Then feel the muscles next to the off-center spines. Attend to the tightest muscles.

A fast way to check for low-back pain in your dog is to stand behind him, grasp both thighs, and lift up the rump (Fig. 7-8 a, b). A pain-free dog will allow you to do this with no objections. Another way to test for low-back pain is to firmly press on each spine. If your dog shows signs of pain in a particular bone, take note of it. Also note that you can lift the dog's front legs into "dance" position to assess low-back pain,

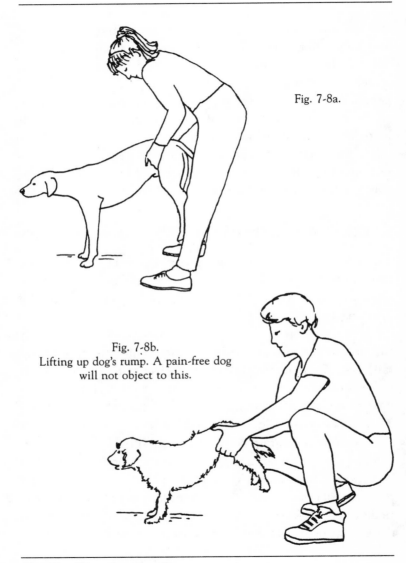

Fig. 7-8a.

Fig. 7-8b.
Lifting up dog's rump. A pain-free dog
will not object to this.

but this can be dangerous to you: the dog may be heavy or unsteady, and you can strain your own lower back.

## CHECKING FOR HIP PAIN & SUBLUXATIONS

At issue here is the hip socket (Fig. 7-9 a, b). Have your dog lay on one side. Hold him down with one hand, grasp his thigh with the other, and raise it up (Fig. 7-10). If this maneuver produces a popping sound, or if your dog shows signs of pain, then he has a painful hip or possibly hip dysplasia (where the thigh bone, or femur, doesn't exactly fit into the hip socket). This is common in larger breeds.

Another way to test for hip pain is to have your dog stand on all fours and raise one of his hind legs. If the other hind leg starts to shake, you can bet it's because the hip is unstable.

## CHECKING FOR HIND~LEG PAIN

It is hard to separate the tests for the hind legs and the hips because of their immediate relation to each other, but there are two mini-tests that will help you determine if your dog has hind-leg pain or instability.

The first test is to place a hand underneath each of your standing dog's hind-leg paws and ask yourself which leg has more weight on it (Fig. 7-11). The one with the least weight is the painful side. Now lift up both legs, one at a time. If the lighter leg comes up easier, you've confirmed your results. While you're down there, check the length of the claws. The paw with the longer claws suggests that less pressure (weight) has

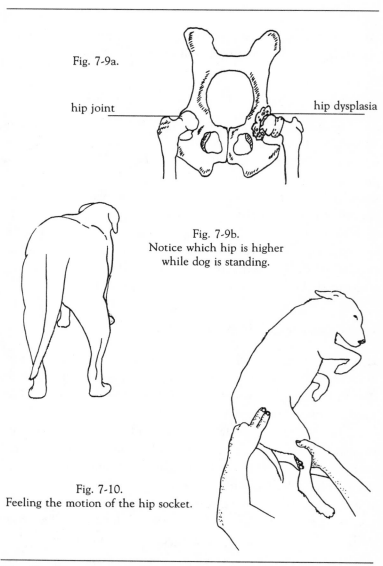

Fig. 7-9a.

hip joint

hip dysplasia

Fig. 7-9b.
Notice which hip is higher
while dog is standing.

Fig. 7-10.
Feeling the motion of the hip socket.

Fig. 7-11.
Feeling which leg the dog is
putting more weight on.

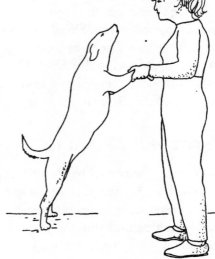

Fig. 7-12.
The wheelbarrow test.
Determines if the hind legs
can support the dog's weight
without teetering.

been put on that foot, as the claws have not worn down.

The second test is called "wheelbarrowing," where you raise the dog's front legs so he is standing up a few inches off the ground. Assist your dog in walking forward a few steps (Fig. 7-12). If he has a painful hind leg, he will immediately start to wobble. The pain could stem from the hip socket or from the leg itself. If you think the leg itself is somehow affected, feel the bones of the hind leg and flex the joints. If you feel no swelling around the joints, and if they bend and open easily, it is probably the hip socket that's distressed.

## CHECKING FOR FRONT~LEG PAIN

The same two tests used to check for hind-leg pain are used to check for front-leg pain. For the "wheelbarrowing" test, raise your dog's hind legs up a few inches so only his front legs are contacting the ground. Walk him forward and sideways a few steps. Your dog should be able to walk these few steps, both straight ahead and to the side, without losing his balance. If he loses balance, he may have front-leg or shoulder pain. Feel each area for muscle tightness and swelling.

## SHORT~LEG ANALYSIS

A leg that appears to be short does not mean the actual leg bone is short, but that a muscular imbalance is present, coupled with a vertebral or hip misalignment. To perform this test, situate yourself behind the standing dog and lift his hind legs up and backwards so he is now standing on just his front legs (Fig.

Fig. 7-13a.
Short-leg analysis.

Fig. 7-13b.
Short-leg analysis—
your perspective.

7-13 a, b). While you're lifting the hind legs, make sure you do this by grasping the legs high on the thighs, close to the abdomen. Now compare the feet. Notice if one leg wants to reflexively pull away from you, or if one leg appears to be shorter than the other. Next, apply a quick "punch" with your fingers into the rump muscles of the short-leg side (the "punch" should be as hard as thumping a watermelon). If the short leg temporarily lengthens and evens out with the other, then the dog may have a low back or hip subluxation on the side of the short leg.

You may also check for neck subluxations during the short-leg analysis. While the dog's legs are extended, as in the example above, have an assistant gently turn the dog's neck to the same side as the short leg. (The dog's nose will be pointing toward the short-leg side.) A short leg that lengthens during this maneuver indicates a neck subluxation on that side. For example, a short right leg that lengthens when the dog turns his head to the right would indicate a subluxation somewhere on the right side of the neck.

# CHAPTER 8

# INTRODUCTION TO THE
# METHODS OF TREATMENT

The methods you are about to learn are a mix of chiropractic and physical-therapy procedures. The goal of the methods is to provide you with tools to help restore normal joint movement for your dog, as well as remove vertebral subluxations.

Relieving nerve pressure throughout your dog's body, especially in his back, has always been the goal of veterinary chiropractic care. Until now, however, there has never been information available to the general public on how to provide this care to their dogs at home. All of the methods presented to you in the following chapters have been tested and re-tested for decades by practitioners of animal chiropractic. While this writer has modified some of the methods for safety purposes (yours and your dog's), they are as close as possible to the original premise and intent.

Because animal chiropractors weren't officially organized until recently, some of the methods here are derived from my investigations into work done by animal chiropractors of the past. And, may I add, some of these old practitioners were tough to find. Of course, the methods have been updated to meet current standards (that is, using the chiropractic methods taught in accredited chiropractic colleges, modified to conform to the canine skeleton).

Dr. Myles Medford, who now resides in Canada and is a true animal-chiropractic pioneer, was kind enough to share many of his time-tested methods with me. Dr. Medford and I share the same chiropractic philosophy: When you tamper with something that works, it is sure to break down.

My discussions with Dr. Medford reinforced my enthusiasm for chiropractic and my confidence in what it can do for both man and beast. Dr. Medford, who at the time of this writing is 69 years young, told me that he has treated dogs suffering from chorea (a nervous disorder characterized by uncontrollable movements in the arms, legs, and face) who have fully recovered after a series of adjustments. These "incurable" dogs would have been put to death by medical veterinarians had it not been for chiropractic.

Many of the following methods center around finding pinched nerves. By feeling the spine and the surrounding muscles, you may detect "hot spots." If, when you press into a spot, the animal flinches, you've probably located a pinched nerve. Hot spots usually cool off within an hour or two after the nerve interference has been removed. A joint that does not move as freely as it should is another sign of nerve impingement.

I'm often asked what percentage of dogs are cured with chiropractic care. This is not an easy question to answer. There are so many different conditions that the question would have to be broken down into number of treatments per specific condition. By and large, chiropractors treat back and neck pain with better than 95 percent success. Success with internal conditions, such as stomach and lung problems, is far more difficult to substantiate, because most animals who receive chiropractic care also receive concurrent medical care. If they heal, both disciplines will want to take the credit. (Of course, it doesn't matter who takes the credit so long as the patient gets better.)

The methods used to remove subluxations in dogs vary according to the comfort and confidence of the practitioner. The manipulative procedures described in the following "method" chapters are fairly tame compared to the more ambitious "cracking" techniques. (The cracking sound you hear during a chiropractic adjustment is gas escaping from a suddenly opened joint.)

One of these original canine adjusting methods is an old neck move that very efficiently opens the communication between the body and the brain by releasing tension between the atlas and the occiput (base of the skull). The importance of this joint (atlanto-occipital joint) cannot be overstated. All neurological impulses produced by the body (muscles, organs, etc.) must pass through this joint so they can be processed by the brain. I refer to this move as the Posterior Atlas Adjustment.

**\*\*Disclaimer:** *This move is for chiropractic professionals and veterinarians only and should not be attempted by dog owners.*

# FEELING THE POSTERIOR ATLAS

Before administering the Posterior Atlas Adjustment, you must determine the location of the first neck bone (atlas). Follow these steps before administering the adjustment.

1. Locate the atlas with the thumb and index finger of one hand by dropping down behind and lateral to the base of the dog's head (occiput). You will feel one very large bump on each side. These are the very palpable and huge atlas wings. **Note:** The dog must be looking straight ahead during this step for an accurate palpation findings.

2. Once your thumb is on one atlas wing and your index finger is on the other, slowly pinch these two fingers together so they remain in constant contact with the atlas, until they meet at the dorsal arch (see Fig. 3-3). You'll be able to feel which finger (thumb or index finger) had to pass over a "hill" first before meeting at the dorsal arch. This higher-feeling side is the posterior atlas side.

3. Note the side of the dog's head/nose tilt. A nose that is pointed more towards the right would indicate a right posterior atlas.

4. Feel the muscles surrounding the atlas wings. The side with the spongier-feeling muscles is usually the side of

the posterior atlas wing.

5. Feel for the "YES" joint (See Chapter 7). The "YES" joint, as you'll recall, is the joint comprised of the atlas and occiput (atlanto-occipital joint). It gives the dog the ability for great flexion and extension, or the "yes" movement. Place your hand on this joint and guide the dog's neck up and down by gently pushing up and down on his chin. If the head veers more to the right, again this would be another indication of a posterior atlas.

## The Adjustment

Follow these steps to deliver the adjustment:

1. With one hand, stabilize (immobilize) the C2 (axis or second neck bone) by gripping the back of the dog's neck with your thumb and index finger so only the atlas is free to move.

2. With your other hand, grasp the dog's nose.

3. Push the dog's nose down towards his chest.

4. Take the neck to tension (removing joint slack) by guiding the dog's nose up towards the opposite (anterior at wing) side. This will be the direction of the thrust. In other words, if the dog's atlas feels higher or is posterior on the right, then his nose will point towards his left during the adjustment.

5. Complete the adjustment by quickly bringing the nose up towards the anterior side in a smooth, circular motion—a quick, but *gentle* "snap." Don't forget, the nose

remains tucked down towards the chest during the adjustment.

Quite often you will hear a "pop" with this move. But remember, popping sounds are not always heard or felt during the adjustment; neither do they attest to the success of the adjustment. Also keep in mind that audibles ("pops") are not noticed nearly as often on a dog as they are on a person.

**Study these methods very carefully before trying any of them on your dog.** Read and re-read the relevant sections several times while picturing the steps in your mind. It's a good idea to practice first on a stuffed animal. True, you won't be able to feel hard bones or tight muscles, but you'll get a good idea of how your own hands and body should be positioned when treating a live animal.

# CHAPTER 9

# METHODS TO HELP YOUR DOG'S NECK

The following procedures may be used on your dog if his neck (cervical vertebrae area) appears to be in pain. Maybe he's not looking straight ahead, or his head is tilted to one side. This is often due to a muscle spasm. Your dog will usually bend his neck to the side that is most comfortable for him; therefore, feel for tight muscles on the opposite side. Sometimes, however, the dog will bend his neck on the spastic side, which helps splint his pain. Remember to feel for hard muscles and hot spots, and for fixed joints that have become areas of decreased movement. This will help you determine which side to adjust.

There are eight easy methods for relieving your dog's neck pain, while at the same time restoring normal movement of the neck.

**METHOD ONE:** Feel the muscles on both sides of your dog's neck by kneeling next to your sitting dog and placing your fingers on each side of the neck (Fig. 9-1). If you feel a harder or tighter muscle on the right side of the neck and the joint feels stuck, then place the side of your right index finger on

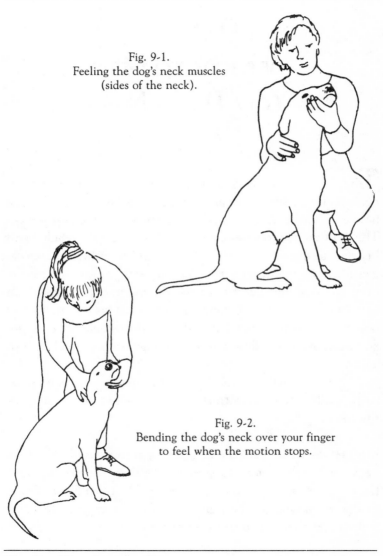

Fig. 9-1.
Feeling the dog's neck muscles
(sides of the neck).

Fig. 9-2.
Bending the dog's neck over your finger
to feel when the motion stops.

that spot. Next, with your left hand, gently bend the neck into your right index finger until the joint's motion stops and you can feel resistance (Fig. 9-2). Retain that tension for about ten seconds. At the end of the ten seconds, deliver a rapid but light impulse with your finger, then immediately release. Repeat this procedure three times for each area. Allow about fifteen seconds between each thrust. This method is useful for any area of the neck, from the base of the skull all the way down to the shoulders.

**METHOD TWO:** This method is similar to the first, and you may use it when your dog appears unable to move or extend his neck upward. **Word of caution:** Before trying this method, be aware here of disc herniation and/or rupture (ask your vet). Dogs with disc herniations keep their heads very low. This method may not be suitable for these dogs.

Feel the back of your dog's neck for tight muscles, from the base of the skull all the way down to the shoulders (Fig. 9-3). Next, while kneeling next to your sitting dog, cup his chin with one hand while grasping the back of his neck between the thumb and index finger of your other hand, right up to the webbing between the fingers (Fig. 9-4). Gently lift your dog's head backwards. Note any areas that "stop" too soon or appear to cause your dog discomfort. If you find one of these spots, zero in on it by placing the web of your hand on that spot while gently pushing the chin up until the movement stops (Fig. 9-5). At the end of this "stop," apply an extra and sudden push up on the chin. This method will help restore backward movement (extension) of the neck.

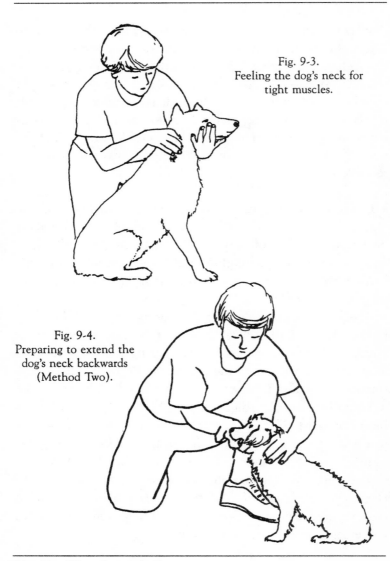

Fig. 9-3.
Feeling the dog's neck for
tight muscles.

Fig. 9-4.
Preparing to extend the
dog's neck backwards
(Method Two).

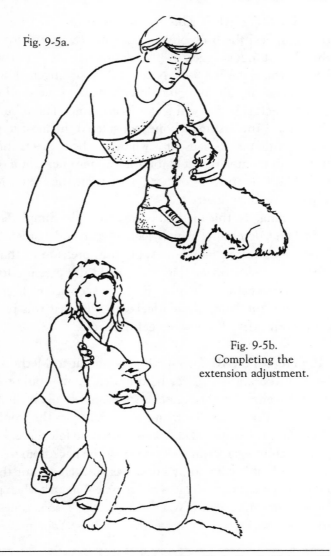

Fig. 9-5a.

Fig. 9-5b.
Completing the
extension adjustment.

**METHOD THREE:** This method is for the first neck bone, the *atlas*. Feel the back of your dog's neck with the tip of your thumb and index finger, as if you're scratching or petting him behind the ears (Fig. 9-6). Next, slide your fingers down from the ears about half an inch below the base of the skull (Fig. 9-7). On each side you will feel a large bump. These bumps are the sides of the first neck bone, considered the most important bone of the spine because it is where the body meets the brain. If there is an impairment of joint movement here, or if one side feels like it is sticking out or bigger than the other, Method Three should be used.

Fortunately, this method is easy to apply. Simply feel each bump and determine which feels bigger and harder (due to toughening of the muscle). Apply firm pressure to that point with your index finger (Fig. 9-8). Hold the pressure for a full ten seconds before releasing. Feel the spot again. If you were successful, the bump should feel softer. Repeat this procedure until both sides of the bone feel the same.

**METHOD FOUR:** This method is similar to Method Three, because you are feeling for hard muscle spots—only this time you are feeling for hard muscles spots anywhere on the back of the neck. (You won't be treating any areas on the front of the neck, simply because neck bones cannot be felt there. Even on people, chiropractors rarely if ever treat the neck from the front.) This method is commonly known as "pressure point therapy." Pressure points are small areas of a muscle that hurt when pressed. When someone is giving you a massage, you'll sometimes notice that certain spots hurt more than others. Your masseur can

Fig. 9-6.
Feeling the dog's atlas
(first neck bone).

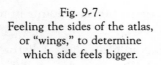

Fig. 9-7.
Feeling the sides of the atlas,
or "wings," to determine
which side feels bigger.

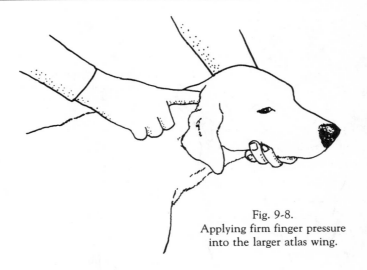

Fig. 9-8.
Applying firm finger pressure
into the larger atlas wing.

press on those spots session after session with the same painful results. This is because these points are stressed each day by a predictable activity pattern. If you're a right-handed baseball pitcher, you'll have a regular muscle knot or pressure point behind your right shoulder. Likewise, if your dog's activities include jerky neck movements, such as those involved in catching a Frisbee, he'll have regular pressure points in related muscle areas on his neck.

Pressure points and "trigger points" aren't exactly the same. Pressure points may simply be hard muscle knots. When you stimulate a pressure point you feel pain at that point. When you stimulate a trigger point, pain or other sensations are felt at that spot, as well as at other areas of the body. For example, pushing a trigger point on the neck will cause pain in the arm.

This is why your dog will sometimes jerk his front leg when you're pressing into a hard muscle on or near the neck.

To use Method Four, feel the back of your dog's neck with your entire hand. You will have to "dig" a little through the fur and skin to feel the muscle condition. Once you feel a hard muscle point, which may also feel warmer than the surrounding muscles, press into it with your finger (Fig. 9-9). As in Method Three, hold your finger against this spot for a full ten seconds, then repeat the procedure until the muscle point feels soft. It is quite possible that you will find several pressure point areas. **A word of caution:** *You should never press into the point so hard that it makes your dog yelp.* A gradual-to-firm finger push is all that's necessary.

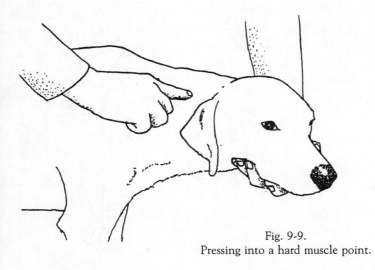

Fig. 9-9.
Pressing into a hard muscle point.

**METHOD FIVE** (Skin Rolling): As in Method Four, you will locate hard muscle points on the back of your dog's neck, but instead of pushing your finger into them, you simply roll the skin over the knots. Using both hands (thumbs and index fingers), lift the skin that's over the hard muscle knot and roll the skin as if rolling a cigarette (Fig. 9-10). Do this until the muscle becomes soft. Even though you are only rolling the skin, the hard muscle beneath it benefits because the method helps release the friction between skin and muscle.

**METHOD SIX** (Skin Lifting): This is similar to Method Five. The only difference is that you lift the skin up as far as its elasticity will allow you to without hurting your dog. You hold the "lift" for ten seconds, then release. Again, this helps to reduce skin-to-muscle friction.

Fig. 9-10.
Skin rolling—relieving
soft-tissue stress.

**METHOD SEVEN** (Pushing the "Spines"): This is a very effective chiropractic move. "Spines" (a.k.a. "spinous processes") are the bony bumps you can feel on the center line along the back of your dog's neck, from the second neck bone to the shoulders (Fig. 9-11). There are seven neck bones, and they all have spines except for the first neck bone, or *atlas*. While sitting next to your dog, feel this entire area by pressing firmly with your fingers. Scan the area several times to get a good idea where the spines are. On some dogs, you won't be able to feel all of the spines, as some of them are either too short or too deeply embedded within the muscles. The spines belonging to the second and seventh neck bones can be felt quite easily. The second neck bone can be felt about two inches below the base of the skull (Fig. 9-12). The sixth and seventh neck bones can be felt where the neck meets the shoulders (Fig. 9-13).

When you feel one of these spines, notice whether any of them point more to one side. If so, use the tip of your thumb or index finger and gently push the spine toward the other side, as though it were a pressure point (Fig. 9-14). At the end of the push, deliver a rapid impulse into that spot. The rapid impulse can be likened to the action those old metal grocery store spring-loaded pricing punches made when the clerk punched the purple ink onto the products. Think of the vertebra to be adjusted as the product, your contact point (finger or thumb) as the ink, and your wrist as the spring-loaded punch, with the speed and force coming from your arm, then releasing (recoiling) as the punch does. You're not "snapping" the bone into place; rather, you are putting it in motion. However, you may feel a slight "pop" during the procedure.

Fig. 9-11.

Fig. 9-12.
Feeling second neck bone.

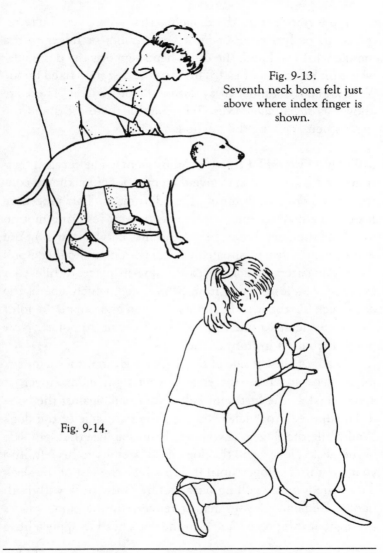

Fig. 9-13.
Seventh neck bone felt just above where index finger is shown.

Fig. 9-14.

You'll notice from the diagrams that whenever you're required to push a bone or push your thumb or finger into a muscle with one hand, the other hand supports the dog somewhere on his body or head. This is so the dog stays fixed in one place and doesn't move away during the procedures. These are known as *stabilization areas*. Take note of these areas and use them when applying the methods.

**METHOD EIGHT** (Traction Adjustment): The cervical traction move was designed to give the practitioner maximum control of the dog's neck during the adjustment. This procedure takes some practice, but is very effective for restoring motion for all of the neck bones below the first cervical (atlas). You will need an assistant situated behind the dog to hold and pull the hindquarters, which keeps the dog in place. While your assistant steadies the dog from behind, feel which side of the dog's neck has the least flexibility. Motion and isolate the joint that flexes least to one side. This is the one to adjust. Now position yourself in front of the dog.

To adjust the *left* side of the dog's neck for a stuck *left* neck joint, place and press the edge of your right index finger, at approximately the first joint below your nail, against the bone to be adjusted. Your left palm cups the right side of the dog's head while the fingers of your left hand stabilize the right side of the neck. Next, bend the dog's head laterally to his left, into your right index finger, until it stops. Take the rest of the slack out of the joint by pulling ("tractioning") the neck with both hands. Remember, your hands remain in the same places throughout this procedure. Turn the dog's head to apply a little more rotation to his left. Once your hands feel solid on these contact areas, quickly pull and thrust in a counterclockwise direction (Figure 9-15). Again, remember that it is speed, not force, that achieves the adjustment. Also, don't forget that this description applies to a left-side adjustment; obviously, you will reverse the procedure for a right-side adjustment. You will often feel or hear a "pop" during this move.

Fig. 9-15.
Preparing for the traction adjustment.

# Chapter 10

# Methods to Help Your Dog's Mid~Back

$S$ome of the methods used in helping your dog's mid-back (thoracic vertebrae area) are similar to those for the neck. After all, you have the same type of structures there, namely muscles and bones. The mid-back, however, feels sturdier than the neck. This is because the middle vertebrae are attached to ribs.

If your dog appears to be uncomfortable in his mid-back, or if he's always trying scratch an itch in his mid-back when there are no fleas, then one or more of the following five methods may be helpful.

**METHOD ONE** (Skin Rolling): As in the neck methods, feel for tight muscle knots on or near your dog's back. You can locate tight muscle points by using both your hands to massage your dog's back muscles, one hand on each side of his back (Fig. 10-1). Take special note of which side has more tight spots. A muscle knot feels like a hard yet spongy bump. It also feels warmer than the surrounding muscles. You may mistake a muscle knot for a rib. A rib, however, feels much harder than even the tightest muscle knot. A hard muscle will still feel spongy to the touch.

Once you've located a muscle knot, simply pick up the skin over the knot with the thumbs and index fingers of both hands and roll this clump of skin as if you were rolling a cigarette (Fig. 10-2). Do this until the point becomes soft. Even though you are not actually bringing the knot up with the skin, the muscle still benefits as you relieve friction between skin and muscle.

**METHOD TWO** (Skin Lifting): This method is almost exactly the same as Skin Rolling. The only difference is that you lift and stretch the skin over the muscle knot as far as the skin's elasticity will allow you to without hurting your dog. Hold for about ten seconds, then release. Repeat the procedure until the muscle underneath the skin becomes soft.

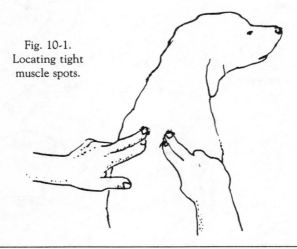

Fig. 10-1.
Locating tight
muscle spots.

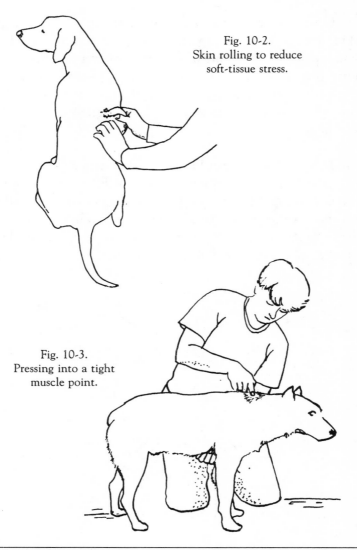

Fig. 10-2.
Skin rolling to reduce
soft-tissue stress.

Fig. 10-3.
Pressing into a tight
muscle point.

**METHOD THREE** (Pressure Points): This is another way to make muscle knots soft. Besides causing your dog pain, a muscle knot puts pressure on the nerves below it. A muscle knot in the middle of your dog's back can hinder his breathing by making his ribs less expansible.

Once you've located a tight muscle point, press your index finger on that point and hold it there for a full ten seconds (Fig. 10-3). Repeat this procedure until the knot becomes soft. Apply this method *at most* once every other day; too much prodding of a muscle can injure it.

**METHOD FOUR** (Pushing the "Spines"): This is a great chiropractic procedure for helping to unpinch nerves. The spines, or "spinous processes," are actually the tops of the mid-back vertebrae. A colossal image of the spines are the large bony plates on the back of a Stegosaurus dinosaur (*cf. King Kong*). To locate the spines of the mid-back, feel the center line of your dog's back, from his shoulders all the way down to where the ribs end a few inches up from his hips, depending on the size of your dog (Fig. 10-4).

Not all of these spines can be readily felt. The ones on the upper part of the back are most easily felt by lifting up your dog's chest while your other hand feels for the spines (see Fig. 10-3). The spines are just a few millimeters apart, so you'll have to run your fingers slowly and carefully down the back. There are thirteen mid-back spines. When your fingers are nearing the end of the mid-back, you'll notice a slight "depression" in place of a spine. This is the eleventh spine, which is smaller than the others.

Fig. 10-4a.

Fig. 10-4b.

Fig. 10-4c.
Feeling the mid-back
spines.

The method is very straightforward. If one of these spines feels off-center, push it back toward the center. Use the tip of your index finger or thumb to firmly push the spine laterally toward the center, and hold that pressure for a full ten seconds (Fig. 10-5). Then apply a little extra push, or "punch," into the spine. Note from the diagram that your other hand is holding the dog on the opposite side from which you are pushing. Use this method for any of the spines that feel off-center. This method should only be used once every three days, so as not to irritate your dog's muscles.

Fig. 10-5.
Pushing a laterally misplaced spine toward the center of the back. Note that the thumb in the diagram is elongated to emphasize that you should use your thumb for this move (it provides a more solid contact).

**METHOD FIVE** (Massaging Over the Nerves): This method is very useful for relieving pressure on the spinal nerves. The nerves of the spinal column lie beneath the spines and a little off to the side. To relieve nerve pressure, deeply massage the muscles just next to the spines of the middle back, all the way down to the last rib area (see Fig. 10-1). A pinched nerve will sometimes "raise its head" in the form of a tight muscle knot next to a spine. You will be massaging all of these small muscle areas next to the spines, but when you find a knot that sticks out, apply deeper pressure, as when treating a pressure point. As long as you apply only moderate pressure to the muscles, you may repeat this procedure every other day.

# CHAPTER 11

# METHODS TO HELP YOUR DOG'S LOW BACK

Your dog's low back (seven lumbar vertebrae) is different from yours in several ways. For one, humans stand erect, creating the "small" of the back, which is really a spinal curve jutting toward the belly. Your dog's low back is curved like his mid-back. If it weren't for the ribs, you might think your dog's back was all one section. A dog's low back has much in common with his neck. Since it is not bound by ribs, the low back is very flexible and therefore prone to injury.

The bulk of a human's body weight rests on the hips and low back during walking. Just the opposite is true for dogs. A dog's body is supported on four legs, much like a table, which lessens the burden on any one part of its back. Dogs support well over half their body weight on their front limbs while walking and running. Also, since dogs don't have to lift anything, their low backs never "go out" like ours. Neither do the discs in a dog's spine "slip" as often as ours, because dogs don't have the same downward forces applied to their spines.

There are six very effective low-back methods you may use to help your dog. The first four are similar to those used for his neck and middle back. The last two methods are exclusively low-back treatments.

**METHOD ONE** (Skin Rolling) and **METHOD TWO** (Skin Lifting): These methods are used throughout the back. Review the two preceding chapters on the neck and middle back.

**METHOD THREE** (Pressure Points): Again, this material was covered in the two preceding chapters. However, there are a couple of notable differences when treating the pressure points of the low back, especially the last two backbones. Applying pressure to these points will also affect your dog's legs, because the nerves that control your dog's legs are located here—so if your dog looks like he's limping from his hind legs, look for pressure points on his low back. Also, if your dog has difficulty squatting while going to the bathroom, it may be due to tight muscle knots on his lower spine. Treat these pressure points every other day until they become soft. When a hard muscle knot becomes soft due to your pressure-point treatment, it means that you were successful in releasing built-up toxins in that muscle. The muscle can "breathe" again.

**METHOD FOUR** (Pushing the "Spines"): As in the previous method chapters, you locate the off-center spines—in this case, of the low back—and push them toward the center. In the low back, some of the spines are flatter and shorter than those of the mid-back.

Once you've located an off-center spine, sit next to your dog on the same side toward which the spine is pointing—

let's say the right. Touch the spine with the tip of your right thumb and push it toward the left while your left hand supports underneath your dog's belly (Fig. 11-1). Sometimes you'll need an assistant to steady your dog from the front so he doesn't jump away during the procedure. This method may be used twice per week.

As always, don't wait for your dog to be in pain before you do treatments. Check and treat for tight muscles and misaligned spines before they become a problem. This is what preventive care is all about.

Fig. 11-1.
Pushing an off-center lumbar spine toward the center.

**METHOD FIVE** (Low-Back Roll, or Lumbar Roll): Those of you who have been to chiropractors for low-back pain may have received a lumbar roll. This is when you are placed on your side, your arms folded at your chest, and the chiropractor grabs hold of your hip and pushes it down toward the table (Fig. 11-2). This common chiropractic procedure can also be performed on your dog. The main difference is that your dog does not have the same type of low-back curvature as you, so that there is far less a chance that your dog has a slipped disc. Dogs, after all, don't lift heavy packages!

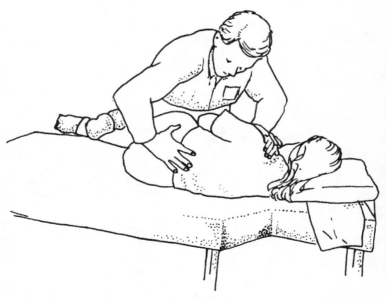

Fig. 11-2.
A human lumbar roll. This move releases lower-back tension.

The low-back roll, or lumbar roll, is a general lower-spine mobilization method, and is not always intended to move any particular spinal bone. However, experience shows that joints of the low-back vertebrae that have been weakened by overactivity are the first joints to move during the lumbar roll.

This method is very easy. Position your dog so he's lying on his back and his hind legs are pointing up (Fig. 11-3). Have an assistant firmly hold the front of your dog to keep him steady in that position. One of your assistant's hands should be placed low on your dog's chest, so the middle back (from the last rib up) doesn't move during the treatment. (Fig. 11-4). Next, hold your dog's hind legs together near the thighs, using both your hands. Then, in one quick

Fig. 11-3.
Positioning the dog
for a lumbar roll.

Fig. 11-4.
Assistant is stabilizing the front of the dog for the lumbar roll.

Fig. 11-5.
Both of the dog's legs are brought down to one side for the lumbar roll.

motion, bring his legs down toward the ground to the opposite side of the off-center spine (Fig. 11-5). Keep them there for about three seconds, then release. You may hear or feel a "pop" during this procedure. This method helps free up the low-back joints. **Important treatment note:** To take further slack out of the low-back joints during this procedure, have your assistant push the front legs in the opposite direction of the hind legs. In other words, if you bring the hind legs down to the right, your assistant will push the front legs to the left in a scissors motion.

If you want to manipulate just the last two low-back bones, use the above method, but this time have your assistant hold your dog a little farther down his belly. This will assure the upper low-back bones don't move.

**METHOD SIX** (Low-Back Extension): This procedure accomplishes a great deal. It relaxes your dog's low-back muscles, gives him greater low-back flexibility, and helps unpinch low-back nerves. The method is a cross between pushing the "spines" and traction, and sometimes requires an assistant.

Position yourself behind your standing dog. With both hands, grab underneath each of his thighs and lift his hindquarters off the ground until you feel a slight tension between the low back and mid-back (Fig. 11-6 a, b). The assistant steadies the front of your dog. Next, place both your thumbs on each side of a low-back "spine," starting with the lowest (seventh lumbar). With each low-back spine, push firmly into each side of the bone as your other four fingers scoop up the dog's body, all the while pulling his hindquar-

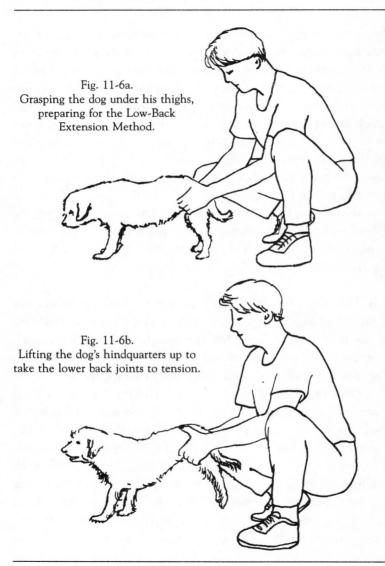

Fig. 11-6a.
Grasping the dog under his thighs, preparing for the Low-Back Extension Method.

Fig. 11-6b.
Lifting the dog's hindquarters up to take the lower back joints to tension.

ters with your arms for traction purposes (Fig. 11-7). Do this for each spine until your reach the ribs. As long as the dog doesn't yelp, you will do him no harm. You may repeat this method daily.

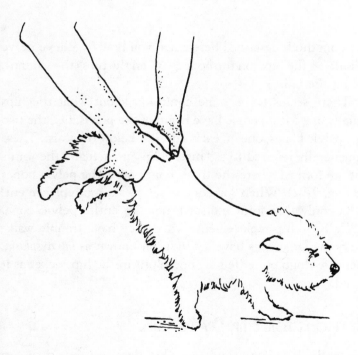

Fig. 11-7.
Pushing into the sides of a lower-back bone with your thumbs while scooping up the dog's body with your palms.

# Chapter 12

# Methods to Help
# Your Dog's Hips and Below

The methods described here teach you how to relieve nerve pressure on the hips, on the bone between the hips (the sacrum), and on the tail.

There seems to be some confusion about what the hips actually are. Most people have heard of the pelvis, i.e., the two large pelvic bones, one on each side, just below the waist. These are generally referred to as "hips." Hips are actually the joints that are formed where the thigh bones meet the pelvic bones (see Fig. 7-9a). When someone undergoes a hip replacement, he has only that joint replaced, not the entire pelvic bone. People have hip replacements when they have trouble walking. Some large dogs have a condition known as *hip dysplasia*, when the thigh bone (femur) doesn't fit in the hip socket as it should.

## Methods for Hip Dysplasia

The methods below cannot cure hip dysplasia, but they can ease the pain of certain types of lameness and low-back pain, or may be used to increase low-back and hip-joint flexibility in an old dog. Methods such as Skin Rolling, Skin Lifting, and Pressure Point Therapy may be used to treat the hip. There are three additional methods that you may find helpful in relieving pain in your dog's hindquarters:

**METHOD ONE** (Hip-Joint Pull): This method is designed to give your dog a break from hip pain due to hip dysplasia, over-exertion of the hips, or limping due to low-back pain. Determining which hip is ailing is usually not a problem. Either your veterinarian has told you your dog has hip dysplasia on one side, or your dog always favors (puts less weight on) one leg or hip.

Fig. 12-1.
Dog is lying on his side with the painful side up.
You examine the dog's hips in this position.

Once you know the affected side, position your dog so he's lying on the opposite side, i.e., painful side up (Fig. 12-1). Next, grasp the thigh on the affected side as high up as possible, gripping the thigh near the rump. Your other hand holds the rest of the rump down (Fig. 12-2). With the hand that's holding the thigh, pull toward yourself in an even, steady, circular manner. Do this for about ten seconds, then release. Now apply firm finger pressure into the hip joint itself, as with a pressure point. Hold this point for another ten seconds. Have the dog lie there for at least a minute before he gets up. This will give his muscles a chance to relax.

Fig. 12-2
Gripping the thigh as you adjust the hip joint.

**METHOD TWO** (Hip Roll):
A hip roll is a maneuver used to create more motion and flexibility in the hip joint, and in another joint between both pelvic bones, called the *sacro-iliac* (Fig. 12-3).

Fig. 12-3.
Feeling the sacro-iliac joint.

Position your dog on his side in the same manner as in Method One (painful side up). Hold your dog's rump (on the painful side) with one hand and grasp his thigh as high as you can with your other hand (See Fig. 12-2). In one quick motion, push the dog's rump toward his head as your other hand pulls the thigh backwards, i.e., toward you (Fig. 12-4 a-c). Release. Have your dog lie there for an additional minute to help relax his muscles.

Fig. 12-4a.
The hip roll.

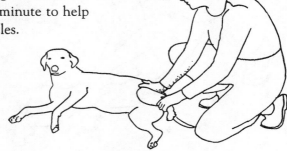

Fig. 12-4b.

Fig. 12-4c.
Different perspectives
of the hip roll.

**METHOD THREE** (Ligament Push): This is not a joint maneuver, but a very specific pressure point. This method is also known as Logan Basic Technique, and is such an effective means of balancing the entire body that one chiropractic college (Logan College of Chiropractic in St. Louis, Missouri) developed a whole teaching system around this procedure.

The pressure point is located on the long, *sacrotuberous*, ligament (Fig. 12-5). The point is near the dog's anus, directly below the base of the tail (Fig. 12-6). If you wish, you may use a rubber glove on the hand that presses this point. The side you push on can often be determined by the direction of the

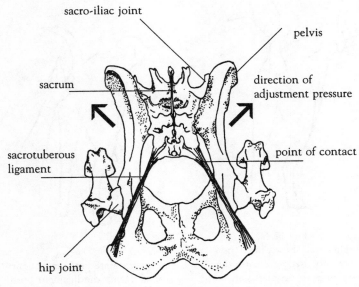

Fig. 12-5.
Sacrotuberous ligament (*back view of dog*).

tail. Observe your dog while he's standing on all fours. When there is hip pain, a dog's tail will often list to one side. If the tail is pointed more toward the right, then your ligament contact is on the right.

For this method, sit behind your standing dog. Contact the ligament (as shown in Fig. 12-5) with your right thumb (if the tail is pointed toward the right) and apply light to medium

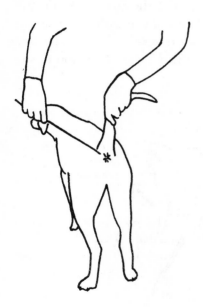

Fig. 12-6.
The stick shown here (not actually used) indicates the ligament push contact point—the point your thumb contacts during the treatment.

Fig. 12-7.
Approximate position of your hand during the ligament push. The rest of your fingers should actually be on the dog's rump.

pressure for a full minute. The pressure you apply is, in this case, in the direction of the dog's right ear (Fig. 12-7). While applying this pressure, massage the surrounding rump muscles (which are often twitching in response to this treatment) with your other hand. For chronically pained dogs, you may use this method daily for two weeks, or until you obtain positive results.

## OTHER METHODS

**METHOD FOUR** (Sacrum Push): The *sacrum* is the bone immediately below the last low-back (lumbar) vertebra. You can't always feel this bone, because it is recessed between the two pelvic bones. However, you can still apply pressure to it to relieve low-back pain. Pushing on the sacrum is helpful because it forces the bone down and acts as a lever to traction the low-back joints.

This method is also easy to do. Sit next to your dog on either side. Feel the tops of both pelvic bones and imagine a spot in between them (See Fig. 12-3). Place one hand underneath your dog's belly and lift up. With the index finger or thumb of your other hand, push down into the space where the sacrum lies (Fig. 12-8 a,b). Hold the pressure for thirty seconds, then release.

**METHOD FIVE** (Tail Traction): We've all done this procedure as kids, intentional or not. Tail Traction is a traction procedure that helps relieve pain in the tail. If you see your dog biting or chasing his tail, he may be in pain. Tail-biting could

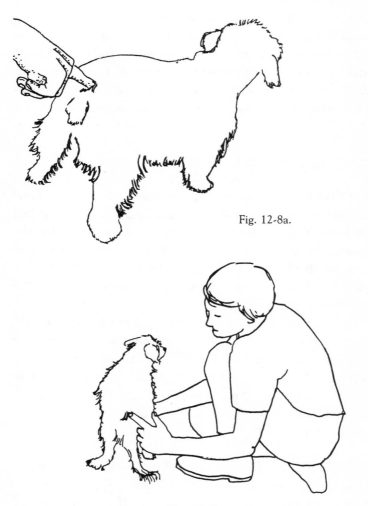

Fig. 12-8a.

Fig. 12-8b.
Pushing the space where the sacrum lies.

also be a sign of serious illness.

There is, of course, a correct way to pull the tail without hurting the tail joints. (Yes, the tail is composed of very small bones that become even smaller as the tail tapers off.) To relieve pressure on the tail: Hold the rump still with one hand. With your other hand, grasp the tail firmly at the base (root), where it comes off the rump, and rotate with a gentle circular motion for ten seconds (Fig. 12-9 a, b). At the end of the ten seconds, apply a firm tug.

To provide traction to the tapering parts of the tail, it is important to work on as few bones as possible at one time. Hold each small section of the tail firmly at both ends to isolate it (Fig. 12-10).

**Caution:** Never *yank* the dog's tail. This is a gradual, low-force move.

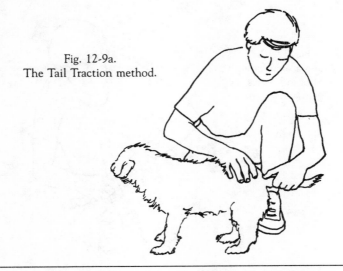

Fig. 12-9a.
The Tail Traction method.

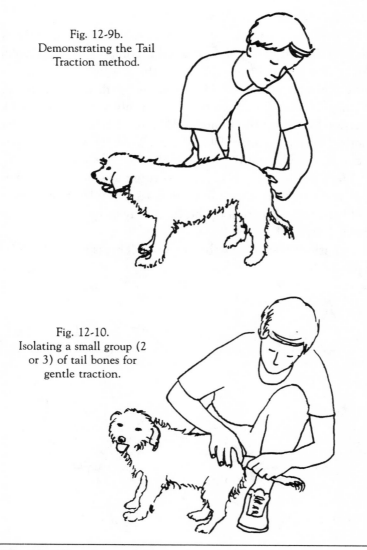

Fig. 12-9b.
Demonstrating the Tail
Traction method.

Fig. 12-10.
Isolating a small group (2
or 3) of tail bones for
gentle traction.

# CHAPTER 13

# METHODS TO HELP
# YOUR DOG'S OTHER JOINTS

This chapter teaches you how to perform simple manipulations of your dog's jaw, shoulder blades, elbow, wrists, and ribs. Review the previous methods for muscle-knot, or pressure-point treatments, because they all apply here.

The joints, other than those of the spine, are referred to as the "extremities." It is important to keep the extremities limber; a stuck jaw, for example, can and does cause neck pain. Pain in the limbs will cause your back to hurt. When foot pain makes you limp, your back compensates with unnatural positions, thus creating back pain until the foot heals.

## THE JAW

Dogs, like people, have one moveable joint on their head, the jaw joint, which works like a hinge and can move out of position for a variety of reasons, including missing teeth and tight jaw muscles. You or someone you know may be afflicted with a condition known as TMJ (or TMD—Temporomandibular Joint/ Disease), where the lower jaw is not properly aligned with the upper jaw. People suffering from this condition often visit their dentist to be fitted with a bite plate to help align their jaw.

For less serious TMJ conditions, people often visit chiropractors. Sometimes the jaw joint is just a little stuck and can be improved with manipulation. The same applies to dogs.

The first step is to determine whether your dog's jaw is misaligned, and if so, on which side. A quick visual inspection is usually all you need. Sit in front of your dog. If you have determined his jaw is misaligned to the right, place your hand on the right bottom part of the jaw, hold his head still with your other hand, and apply a quick push from right to left (Fig. 13-1). Hold the jaw in place for ten seconds before releasing.

You may even feel the jaw pop into place where the jaw meets the head, just in front and a little below the ears.

Fig. 13-1.
Checking jaw alignment.

## THE SHOULDER BLADES

Because a dog carries more than half its weight on its front limbs, the muscles surrounding the shoulder blades are often tight and need to be loosened. The shoulder blade to be treated is on the same side as the affected front leg.

Feel for one of the shoulder blades by placing your hand just to the right or left of your dog's upper back (Fig. 13-2). Your fingers can feel the vague bumpy outline of the shoulder blade by pressing firmly into the surrounding muscles. Once you have located the shoulder blade, place the palm of your

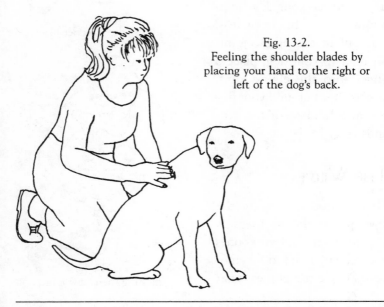

Fig. 13-2.
Feeling the shoulder blades by placing your hand to the right or left of the dog's back.

hand on it, making sure the hand position doesn't move. Then, with your other hand, grasp high on the front leg on the same side and lift up suddenly (Fig. 13-3). Note: the front leg should already be flexed or bent, not straight, when you perform this move.

## The Elbow

This is a basic traction move. If you notice your dog limping on one of his front legs, manipulate the elbow joint. Sit next to your dog, place a finger into the elbow joint, flex the joint around your finger, and hold for a few seconds (Fig. 13-4).

## The Wrists

This method is used for the lower part of the front legs. A dog has seven small wrist bones (carpi), which aid in locomotion. People sometimes suffer

Fig. 13-3.
Adjusting the shoulder blade.

Fig. 13-4.
Adjusting the elbow joint.

from a condition known as "carpal tunnel syndrome," where a nerve is pinched between the wrist bones, causing pain. It is often brought on by prolonged repetitive wrist movements, such as typing on a computer. Even though this syndrome is rare with dogs, their wrist bones will at times get jammed. A dog who limps needs to have his wrist manipulated.

Feel your dog's wrist, which is located under the forearm bones known as the *ulna* and *radius* (see Fig. 3-8a). As a unit, the wrist bends quite easily. Grasp the affected paw with both your thumbs and index fingers, as if to give your dog a manicure. Start out by pulling the paw toward you (traction), and at the same time bend the paw in both directions, about ten bends per session (Fig. 13-5). While working the wrist area, you may want to see if the toes/digits or phalanges need loosening up. If so, then grasp them like you would the wrist and gently traction them in an up and down fashion.

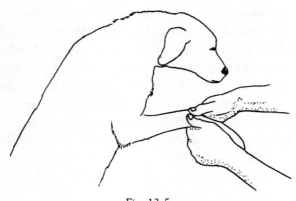

Fig. 13-5.
Tractioning the paw to adjust the wrist.

# The Ribs

If your dog shows signs of labored breathing, the ribs my not be expanding properly. This is sometimes due to muscle spasms at the places where the ribs meet the mid-back bones (thoracic vertebrae), or where they meet the chest bone (sternum).

Walk or run with your dog for a few minutes until his breathing is heavy. (He should not have a muzzle on for this procedure, since a dog cannot breathe as deeply when muzzled.) Then place both hands on his mid-back. Note whether one side expands a little less than the other during inhalation. If so, feel the muscles and "rib bumps" just to the left or right of the "spines." If one feels higher, apply firm finger pressure (Fig. 13-6a, b). Continue applying this pressure until your dog has taken fifteen or more deep breaths. (Your dog is, in effect, assisting with his own treatment.) Now turn your dog around so he's lying on his back. Place your hand on his chest bone and allow him to take some deep breaths. Feel the sides of the chest bone (sternum) with your fingertips. This is where the front part of the ribs meet. If you notice an elevation here, apply firm finger pressure and wait for your dog to take several more deep breaths.

As always, before attempting any sort of manipulation on your dog, consult your veterinarian to make sure there are no broken bones or other serious conditions.

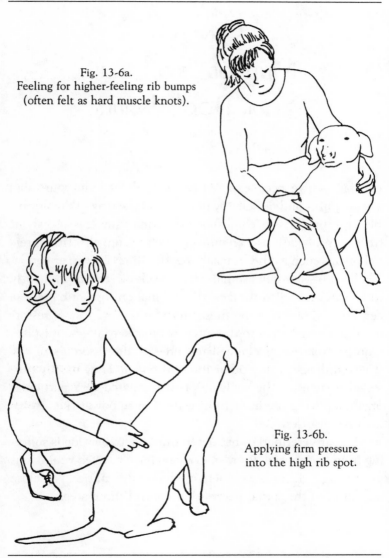

Fig. 13-6a.
Feeling for higher-feeling rib bumps
(often felt as hard muscle knots).

Fig. 13-6b.
Applying firm pressure
into the high rib spot.

# CHAPTER 14

# METHODS TO HELP YOUR DOG'S INSIDES

So far, you've been exposed to methods to help your dog's aching joints and muscles by finding and treating subluxations. But chiropractic is not only about treating pain. It is also about treating subluxations to remove nerve pressure affecting internal organs such as the stomach, heart, kidneys, liver, et cetera.

Each of your dog's spinal nerves leads directly or indirectly to an internal organ. In fact, the original chiropractic premise centered around treating these areas for the purpose of restoring the power source to the internal organs. Make no mistake, chiropractors never claimed to cure specific disorders of the stomach, liver, or any other internal organ. They merely professed to remove the subluxation that related to a particular organ, allowing the body to heal itself once power (i.e., nerve impulse) was restored.

If your veterinarian has determined that your dog is suffering from an internal disorder, or if you have noticed your dog is not eating right or is experiencing bowel difficulties, pay close attention to the spinal nerves that control those areas.

**METHOD ONE:** Each spinal area (spinal nerve) leads directly or indirectly to a specific organ. If you suspect your dog is suffering from stomach problems, for example, then feel for tight muscle knots or off-center "spines" at the middle part of his back, specifically at the fifth, sixth, seventh, and eighth thoracic vertebrae (Fig. 14-1a).

You'll also notice from the charts (Fig. 14-1b) that sometimes an organ, such as the stomach or heart, can be stimulated by adjusting different parts of the back. One chart is titled "Sympathetic," the other "Parasympathetic." These terms refer to the parts of the autonomic nervous system, which works without you having to think about it (i.e., enabling you to

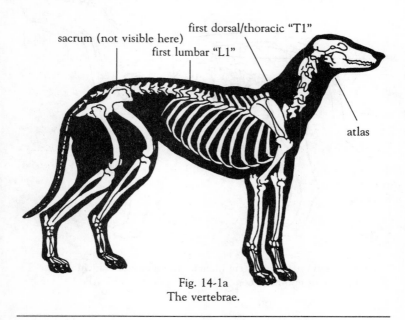

Fig. 14-1a
The vertebrae.

breathe, or digest food, while you sleep). Adjusting the stomach areas found on the Parasympathetic chart will stimulate the stomach's function by increasing the amount of acid it produces, while relaxing the muscles around the rectum. The heart will calm down when you adjust the parasympathetic areas and speed up when you adjust the sympathetic areas.

Once you have found one of these spots by using the methods described in Chapters 7 and 10, treat the spot with pres-

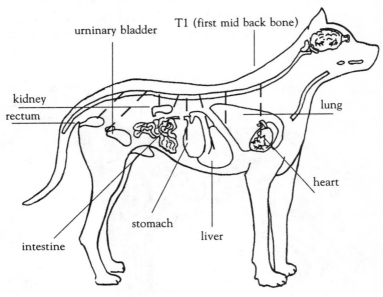

Fig. 14-1b.
The sympathetic nervous system includes those nerves branching from T1 (first thoracic or mid-back bone) all the way down to L7 (the last lumbar or low-back bone).

sure, or with a light adjustment. If your dog is seriously ill, these spots may be treated daily until the subluxation has been lessened or removed. Note that even when the subluxation is removed, it still may take several days before you notice an improvement in your dog's health.

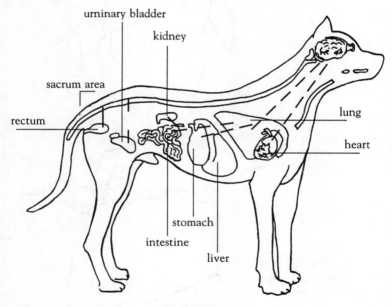

Fig. 14-1c.
The *parasympathetic* nervous system includes those nerves branching from near the base of the skull (actually emanating from *cranial nerves*—nerves arising from inside the skull), and those branching from the area of the sacrum.

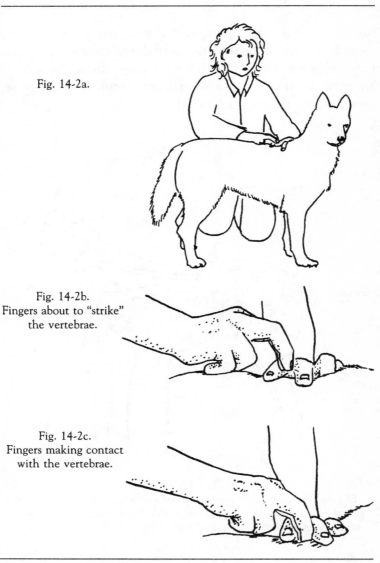

Fig. 14-2a.

Fig. 14-2b.
Fingers about to "strike"
the vertebrae.

Fig. 14-2c.
Fingers making contact
with the vertebrae.

**METHOD TWO:** Another way to treat spinal subluxations so as to affect the organs is to vigorously stimulate the areas directly over the appropriate "spines." To do this, place the index and middle fingers of one hand on each side of the spine (Fig. 14-2 a–c). Next, with the index and middle fingertips of your other hand (pressed together as one), thump that spine about a dozen times in quick succession, then deeply massage both sides of the spine for a few more seconds. You may apply this method to all the subluxations you find.

Finally, remember that your dog is entitled to more than one illness. This means that he may have several internal conditions at one time, and therefore multiple subluxations. Treat them all. Wherever you find signs of a subluxation, adjust it. If it's not causing a problem now, it will in the future. And remember, healing takes time.

**METHOD THREE:** This method can be used in *place* of almost all the methods described in this book. It involves using a device called a metal mallet or an activator (Fig. 14-3). This instrument is a spring-loaded adjusting tool that is generally regarded as safe for most spinal and extremity adjustments. It emits just ounces of pressure at the tip when squeezed.

To use the metal mallet, adjust the tension by screwing or unscrewing the top and place the tip on the bone in the direction of the thrust. The amount of thrust or tension is usually set stronger for larger bones. Once the instrument is in place, then squeeze the mechanism to release the thrust (Fig. 14-4 a, b). (Information on how to buy a metal mallet can be found at the end of this book.)

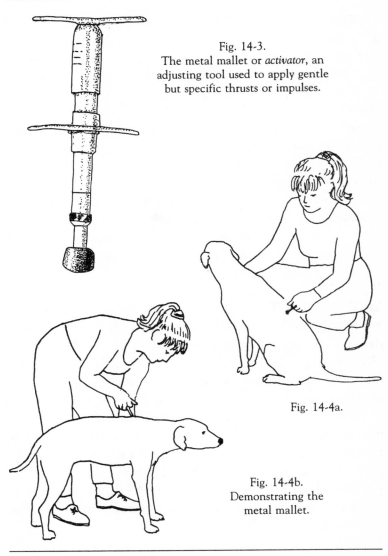

Fig. 14-3.
The metal mallet or *activator*, an adjusting tool used to apply gentle but specific thrusts or impulses.

Fig. 14-4a.

Fig. 14-4b.
Demonstrating the metal mallet.

# CHAPTER 15

# CASE MANAGEMENT AND CASE HISTORIES

*S*ince you've decided you want to help your dog with chiropractic methods, you should know a few particulars about managing your patient. Keep in mind that you are managing only the subluxations, *not* a medical condition. You therefore have some decisions to make:

### Is the dog a candidate for chiropractic care?

The answer is yes only if you rule out *all* the contraindications to performing the methods (see Chapter Four).

### Which back areas do you adjust?

Only those areas that are subluxated. Some use the "pop and pray" method of moving as many bones as they can in the hope of stumbling into the right one. This is not considered true chiropractic; rather, it is an attempt to show off to your friends that you can "move those bones," and should be avoided.

### How often should you adjust your dog?

You should generally wait one or two days after the first treatment to adjust again. This gives the body time to heal. However, you should check your dog for subluxations weekly.

### Which adjusting techniques do you use?

All of the techniques described in this book are effective for removing subluxations. The one with which you feel most comfortable is the one to use. The second criterion is "What is best for your patient?" A very sore dog will not appreciate being adjusted all the time. However, gentle pressure-point methods can be used almost every day.

### Should you adjust a dog who exhibits no symptoms?

The answer is yes. This is known as maintenance care. Once you know how to adjust, the dogs with whom you come in contact should be checked regularly for subluxations, to prevent lameness and promote overall good health.

### Should you tell your veterinarian about your dog's chiropractic care?

Again, the answer is yes. The best possible scenario is that the veterinarian is educated in chiropractic care and that you work together to provide complete health care for your dog. Your veterinarian provides medical insight and background that is vital to your dog's health.

### What can you expect from the treatment?

This is always *the* question. The best you can do is deliver a safe and effective adjustment, and let the body do the rest. Sometimes the body performs miracles, or fast cures. But a pinched nerve may have been disturbing your dog's body for months or years. Nature takes its sweet time to heal. It could be days, weeks, or months before your dog is healed to his full potential.

## SOME CASE HISTORIES

1. A four-year-old German shepherd named French was presented to me for what his owners described as "delirium." The dog would go into violent fits of rage for no particular reason, thrashing his head about, nipping at anyone in range, running around the yard in a haphazard pattern, then calming down for a while before going into his tirade again. This had been the pattern for three weeks. My examination revealed no hind-leg lameness, no signs of hip dysplasia, and no mid-back subluxations. Upon further investigation, I found out that the owners had just switched to a choker collar for training purposes, which French did not like. The previous collar had been a simple leather collar. The veterinarian had given the dog medication (muscle relaxers) and advised the owners to house-rest French for one week—not to let him run around the yard. Upon further examination, I found pronounced muscle tightness and lack of motion around the first and second cervical vertebrae. The chiropractic treatment consisted of light muscle massage, then deep muscle massage and a light rotary adjustment of the first and second cervical vertebrae. The delighted owners called the next day and told me that French had yet to have an episode. After two more adjustments, two days apart,

French had no more episodes, and the owners got rid of the choker.

2. "Sue," a seven-year-old collie, was presented to me for exhibiting lethargy. She couldn't eat, had no energy, and was losing weight. She had been under veterinary care for five weeks with no results. Sue's vet had performed various gastrointestinal testing, but the results were inconclusive. There was no history of injury or food poisoning. However, Sue had gotten loose from the backyard for ten minutes about the time she came down with these symptoms. Her owner assumed that she had chased a rabbit and strained her back. The chiropractic examination revealed a definite subluxation at the sixth and seventh thoracic area, and a subluxation on the right side of the atlas. I adjusted these areas with pressure-point therapy to relieve the muscle knots, including a light thumb adjustment to the thoracic "spines," as well as to the right wing of the atlas. Sue stayed inside for a week, as prescribed by the vet, and after four adjustments over eight days, was up and around again. Sue was symptom-free after two weeks.

3. A five-year-old Rottweiler named Sergeant was presented to me for severe right-hip lameness. Sergeant had long had a mild case of hip dysplasia affecting his right hip, but it had never been this bad. He had been almost completely lame for three weeks. The case his-

tory revealed no recent traumas. Examination of the right hip did, indeed, show signs of hip dysplasia, and further examination revealed a marked area of muscle tightness in the middle and lower lumbar spine. No foreleg or hindleg lameness was found. I adjusted the fifth, sixth, and seventh lumbars with an easy "roll" move, noticing a distinct "popping" sound each time. I applied light massage to the affected area. Sergeant appeared to feel better almost immediately, but still had a distinctive limp. I adjusted him every day for a week, and every other day during the next week. The same subluxations kept recurring, but were reduced with each adjustment. After a full two weeks had passed, Sergeant was completely recovered. I learned that when Sergeant's usual sleeping place, his owner's bed, was declared off limits, he had been forced to find different sleeping quarters—namely a laundry room with a tile floor. In the interests of preventive medicine, Sergeant was given his own mattress!

# CHAPTER 16

# THE FUTURE OF ANIMAL CHIROPRACTIC

The future of animal chiropractic is as bright as the success of interprofessional relationships, primarily between the veterinary and chiropractic state boards. The ideological distance between these two healing arts is not as great as that between chiropractors and the American Medical Association. Like the AMA, the various veterinary societies are very political. However, the veterinarians themselves seem to be quite open-minded.

There is an organization, the American Veterinary Chiropractic Association (AVCA), that offers certification to both chiropractors and veterinarians, as well as to students of each. However, the AVCA has no state recognition, and their certificate does not legally qualify the recipient to practice animal chiropractic.

Technically, veterinarians can already practice chiropractic on animals, even without taking a course.[1] Chiropractors, on

---

[1] I received a letter from Maryland's State Board of Veterinary Medical Examiners on July 8th, 1996. Apparently, one of their members had objected to an animal chiropractic seminar I gave in Maryland one weekend. After "Dear Dr. Daniel Kamen," the letter stated: "It has been brought to our attention that you are offering animal chiropractic seminars in Maryland. In Maryland our regulations define the practice of veterinary medicine to include 'the

the other hand, no matter how qualified, are forbidden to practice chiropractic on animals in most states. There are no states that allow chiropractors to treat animals, but some states are more serious than others about enforcing their laws. My advice to chiropractors who wish to work on animals is to first check with their own state's professional regulators. Some states will allow chiropractors to work on animals under the guidance of a licensed veterinarian.

Veterinary colleges do not currently teach spinal manipulation, as do some human medical colleges. But there has been a dramatic increase in veterinary students who are interested in animal chiropractic. It is only a matter of time before they infiltrate their schools and associations, moving animal chiropractic to the forefront of veterinary academics. The alternative is for chiropractic colleges to teach veterinary subjects and qualify future chiropractors to treat ani-

---

practice by any person who diagnoses, advises, prescribes, or administers a drug, medicine, biological product, appliance, application, *or treatment of any nature* [emphasis added], for the prevention, cure, or relief of a wound, fracture, bodily injury or disease of animal' (2-301.f.1). The regulations from the chiropractic board in Maryland limit its application by a Doctor of Chiropractic to treatments for the human body only and does not include animals." [Author's note: This is true of most states, although some states allow chiropractors to work on animals under the supervision of a licensed veterinarian.]

The letter continued: "Since the practice of animal chiropractic is limited to veterinarians only in the state of Maryland, our Board requests that you inform the participants in your seminars that, in Maryland, the information they learn about animals can only be used on their *own* animals or by a veterinarian licensed in the state of Maryland. We also trust that you are not using live animals in your seminars for demonstrations as this could be a violation of our practice act."

mals. This seems improbable, however, because all of the current state laws would have to be rewritten.

Chiropractic is now one hundred years old, having survived attack after brutal attack from the AMA. Why? Because chiropractic works! And the people who know about chiropractic want it for animals, too.

In this writer's opinion, the general population will find it difficult to find a convenient animal chiropractor for at least another twenty years. It is important, therefore, that animal trainers, breeders, groomers, and owners learn how to perform some chiropractic themselves. The goal of this book is to fill the void, at least temporarily.

# Appendix A

# Common Orthopedic Conditions Affecting Dogs

| Condition | Breed |
|---|---|
| Carpal subluxation (wrist) | Irish Setter |
| Cervical vertebral deformity (misshaped neck bones, a.k.a. spondylolisthesis) | Basset Hound, Great Dane, Doberman Pinscher |
| Elbow joint malformation | Afghan Hound |
| Hip dysplasia | Most large breeds, such as German Shepherds |
| Intervertebral disc degeneration | Cocker Spaniel, Dachshund, Beagle, Pekinese |
| Patellar (knee) luxations | Toy breeds |
| Short spine | Shiba Inu (Japan), Greyhound |
| Spina bifida | English Bulldog |
| Wobbles (wobbly gait) | Doberman, Great Dane, Rottweiler, Basset Hound |

Not all of the above conditions can be successfully treated with chiropractic care. Chiropractic will not *cure* dogs suffering from hip dysplasia, for example. However, low-back pain due to the low-back muscles compensating for hip dysplasia can be helped by using the methods in this book. Again, you aren't always treating the disease, but the patient who *has* the disease.

Another example of treating the patient rather than the disease would be the dog with "wobbles" (a.k.a. cervical vertical instability). With wobbles there is a stenosis, or narrowing of the vertebral canal, in the lower part of the neck, often caused by a congenital malformation. The dog exhibits a wobbly gait and limb instability. Because the dog is straining to walk, subluxations of the spine (especially of the neck) are often associated with wobbles. Chiropractic therapy, while it doesn't offer a cure for wobbles, can help slow down some of the symptoms associated with the disease.

Intervertebral disc degeneration—or, for that matter, diseases of the disc in general—cannot be cured with chiropractic therapy. However, the unaffected areas of the spine (those with no disc disease) can still be treated by skilled practitioners. A permanent spinal condition at one location will almost always cause subluxations elsewhere in the spine.

## Conditions Successfully Helped by Chiropractic

Conditions that are *helped* by chiropractic care are not always *cured*. For example, while neck pain can be readily helped by chiropractic treatment, it usually comes back. I'm often asked by my human patients if their back pain will return once I've fixed it. The answer is usually yes—particularly when the same set of circumstances exists now as existed when they first experienced the pain. Altering your occupation, lifestyle, or exercise routine may help prevent pain and subluxations, but prevention isn't infallible.

Among the canine conditions helped by chiropractic care are:

1. **Back and neck pain.** Chiropractic care is especially helpful when an offending collar is replaced by a non-injurious one.

2. **Front-leg pain and lameness.** Conditions of this nature that are not caused by fractures or disease can often be helped by treating subluxations in the lower part of the neck and in the upper part of the back.

3. **Fevers.** A high fever often responds well to an upper cervical (neck) adjustment. Enhanced communication between the body and brain serves to raise the body's overall resistance against infections. A dog with a high fever should always be looked at by a vet before any chiropractic moves are performed.

4. **Hind-leg pain and lameness.** Low-back adjustments are very successful for treating sciatica (leg pain) and lameness due to muscle spasms.

5. **Organ dysfunction associated with acute musculo-skeletal onset.** This does not mean a direct injury to a specific internal organ, but refers to the fact that an internal condition noticed soon after a back injury can often be helped through chiropractic methods. For example, if you notice your dog has difficulty with bladder control after falling off a high platform, look for low-back subluxations. It is important to stress that such conditions respond best when treated immediately after an accident—provided, of course, that there are no factors contraindicating an adjustment (see Chapter 4). Organs and subluxations that are ignored following an injury can result in degeneration of the

tissues, which makes conservative care, such as a chiropractic adjustment, less effective, or possibly ineffective. In any case, find the subluxations, treat them, and find a veterinarian to work with you. Removing subluxations will *always* improve the health of your dog.

# Appendix B

# Chiropractic and the Eye of the Beholder

The first article presented below appeared in the *Foundation Head News*, a Palmer School of Chiropractic publication, in 1921. It was reprinted from an article in the *Journal of the American Medical Association* titled "Chiropractors Hereby Warned to Quit Adjusting Mules, Cows and Dogs—Positively It Won't Do." It is not clear who "Old Bones" was, but judging by the context of the article, it is obvious he was a an early detractor of chiropractic and, very likely, an agent of the AMA.

Whether or not this opinion impeded the acceptance and progression of animal chiropractic is still unclear. But the second article—from the front page of the *Wall Street Journal*, Monday, July 13, 1987—shows that animal chiropractic made very little headway in that 66-year timespan. I include these two articles as a sort of second opinion, trusting that well-informed readers can reach their own conclusions and will make up their own minds about this issue.

## "A VETERINARY CHIROPRACTOR"
### by "Old Bones"

In preceding generations a veterinary, usually dubbed a horse doctor, was more often than otherwise a pickup who owned or loafed around a livery stable, possessing a supposed mysterious knowledge of animal diseases, the knowledge being dispensed from horse heaven and having no connection whatever with science. A great change for the better has resulted from the establishment of good schools of veterinary medicine throughout the country, in the matter of which our own state ranks well to the front. Young men of clean morals and good social standing have been attracted to this profitable and honorable work, and, by their gentlemanly conduct, have done much to elevate the profession to a legitimately higher plane.

A cursory glance at the curriculum for a course in veterinary medicine, with a mere scanning of the scientific textbooks used to provide a student with the necessary knowledge of the science and art, will quickly convince anyone that, like human medicine, there is enough to employ the keenest minds and more than any one man can hope to compass. In neither branch will the student or practitioner have time or frequent need for writing prescriptions for or the disbursement of booze. Nor will he, if fired by the prime controlling spirit that should prompt the matriculant to enter the field of medicine, either human or veterinary, namely, a sincere desire to ameliorate suffering and prevent disease, ever change his occupation and title from V.S. (Veterinary Surgeon) to D.C.

It will be necessary to explain that the title D.C. has been selected by a class of mercenary mountebanks, presently much in vogue, to designate Doctor of Chiropractic. The wizard of the stage can seem to pull a fat goose from the vest pocket of a tight-fitting dress suit and cause it to lay a life-sized egg as it waddles across the stage. The audience does not know how he does it, but the wizard does. So it is with the foregoing title. Palmer, the handsome founder of the so-called school, knows what it means.

To the careful but unfeeling reader of the rich and rapidly growing literature of this popular fad, cross enough to enjoy a joke at the expense of the suffering, gullible public, the chief interest in the average advertising pamphlet broadcast over the country is the fun of checking up on the palpable lies and absurdities of the claims made. But for the fellow who has made a failure in an honorable vocation, or never had a thought bigger than a dollar, there is balm and lure. He is repeatedly shown and reminded by vivid testimonials that there's money in it right from the start and the future is brilliant, for a sucker is born every minute.

Much of the tempting, juicy literature referred to is furnished by active field men in the form of testimonials sent to the breeding pen at Davenport. It is all interesting, but space will permit the reproduction of only one or two gems.

The following, sent in by a scintillating Georgia graduate, is typical of all and fairly radiates hope and encouragement for the lower animals, including the mule and his co-geners, especially the asinine half of his humble hybrid. He says when he "was adjusting Henry Vinson's son for an incoordination causing pneumonia" that "Mr. Vinson says, 'Doc, I have a mule that is down in the back and can't get up and wish you would come out and see if you can do something for him.'" The versatile chiropractor looked over his new patient and "adjusted the mule between the hip bones." The mule recovered—presumably slowly enough to allow the adjuster to escape. The same practitioner also reports that he "was called to attend Mr. Ben Vandalsem's Scotch Collie, who was dragging his hind legs, and after adjusting the dog he improved and got quite normal." A Texas chiropractor records the interesting case of a "cow down, all swelled up as if she would burst." Diagnosis: "A poisoned condition." Treatment: "I adjusted sixth and eight dorsals and K.P. (Kidney Place). In two minutes cow was up vomiting. I came back in one hour; cow seemingly in normal condition." Having in mind the fact that some states like our own, offer more protection on their statute books for livestock than human beings, one editorial writer is moved to the following bit of irony: "That men, ignorant of the body and its processes, should treat the ailments of men, women and children is apparently a small thing; human life is the only thing involved. But that ignoramuses should trifle with the health of a horse or a hog is an outrage; that is property. If chiropractors are wise they will confine their malpractice to humans; it is safer."

Let there be no mistake as to the attitude of physicians who desire to uphold the honor of medical practice. Knowing well the people's inability to judge the true and the spurious, and realizing the public assumes the chiropractor and his ilk are competitors, but little publicity of sentiment is given by the regular profession. As a matter of fact, dear friends, the income of the doctor is but little affected by the spasmodic jarring of the spine practiced by the chiropractor for every disease imaginable. A large percent of the cases he treats more than once or twice are really mental aberrations associated with hysteria, such cases being treated with due consideration and kindness, but not sought after nor desired by the ethical doctor. These unfortunate patients are often greatly benefitted for a time, and sometimes permanently cured by Chiropractic, Osteopathy, Christian Science, or anything else sufficiently sensational to jar them loose from their enjoyment of ill health.

## A LOVELORN PARAKEET, LAME HORSE FIND ILLS WERE ALL IN THE BONES
### Chiropractic for Animals Is A Fast-Growing Specialty; Some Vets Are Skeptical.
*by Roger Ricklefs*

BUFFALO GROVE, IL—For a chiropractor, manipulating the bones in the neck may be strictly routine. But when the patient is a giraffe, it is a little tougher.

Daniel R. Kamen, a chiropractor here, first climbed up an 11-foot ladder. Then he placed his hands on the giraffe's neck.

Whack! The giraffe swung its powerful neck against Mr. Kamen and knocked him to the ground. "I felt ridiculous, but I wanted to see if it could be done," the 31-year-old chiropractor says.

Touchy giraffes are just one problem facing practitioners of one of the medical world's faster growing specialties, animal chiropractic. A growing number of chiropractors are manipulating (or, as they put it, "adjusting") the bones of horses, dogs, cats, llamas, and parakeets.

At least as a sideline, "several hundred chiropractors now look at Fido as well as his owner," estimates Werner E. Hoff, a Trenton, N.J. chiropractor. This compares with perhaps a dozen when he first tackled an animal's bad back a decade ago, Mr. Hoff says.

## Words of Caution

A few chiropractors now practice on animals full time, including several who are also veterinarians. Mr. Kamen has even started an association of animal chiropractors called "Animal Crackers."

The animal chiropractic field, however, hasn't been universally acclaimed. "We aren't even aware of any body of scientific literature established to prove that chiropractic is useful or not useful for animals," says Arthur Freeman, the executive vice president of the American Veterinary Medical Association. "I don't think veterinary chiropractic has been around long enough," Dr. Freeman adds.

Whatever the strictures, animal chiropractors say they are getting results—even where traditional veterinarians flopped. For instance, an anorexic dog regained its appetite after chiropractic relieved its hind-leg lameness, says Sharon L. Willoughby, a Port Byron, Ill. chiropractor-veterinarian.

Dr. Willoughby says her work has restored a female parakeet's love life. Following a neck injury, the patient sat in the bottom of her cage, didn't eat and didn't move about. Her cage mate— a male—fed her by dropping food in her mouth.

# The Invalid Recovers

"Her bones were so tiny that when I adjusted her neck, I thought I had broken it," Dr. Willoughby says. But within minutes, the invalid started turning her neck to preen her feathers. Though she had never laid an egg before, she soon laid and hatched six. "Chiropractic made her much more amorous," Dr. Willoughby says.

In Buffalo Grove, Michael Soto, a jeweler and racehorse owner, turned to Mr. Kamen when a back problem plunged one of his horses into a losing streak. After the treatment, the horse won $5,000 in one race and $4,500 in another.

Another equine example: Kathryn Sickling, a Chicago businesswoman and horse breeder, recalls a favorite horse made lame by a nerve injury. Three veterinarians prescribed rest, but that didn't help. One vet talked of euthanasia.

Ready to "try anything," she says, Ms. Sickling called in Dr. Willoughby. She also shelled out $80 to have a professional masseur massage her beloved beast. "A week later, I was riding the horse. Nobody could believe it," Ms. Sickling says. "A few years ago, nobody ever thought about chiropractic for animals. So many animals are killed that don't need to be."

Animals chiropractors concede that traditional veterinary techniques often work where theirs would serve no purpose. But Dr. Willoughby says the success others had with chiropractic made her switch careers. After thirteen years as a veterinarian, "I couldn't see why I wasn't getting more animals better," she says. "Sixty-five percent of my income came from giving vaccinations and removing sex organs," she adds. "I was really burned out. I considered going into acupuncture."

Then one of her clients decided to take a chronically lame dog to a chiropractor. "I thought it was pretty silly, but the dog started walking more normally thereafter," Dr. Willoughby says. "This was a turning point in my life."

Dr. Willoughby gave up her veterinary practice and started studying chiropractic to earn her second doctorate. Today, she lives in a large house with a dog, two cats, five chickens, and a goat that likes to walk on her horse's back. She practices chiropractic only on animals.

To work on a horse, Dr. Willoughby climbs up on a couple of bales of hay. Some chiropractors place a padded two-by-four against a large animal's bones and pound the board with a mallet. Dr. Willoughby uses her bare hands. To develop the strength to manipulate a large animal's bones, she had to practice weight lifting.

But the animal chiropractor's worst problem is the law. According to the Veterinary Medical Association's Dr. Freeman, laws in all 50 states restrict medical treatment of animals to veterinarians.

That isn't a problem for practitioners like Dr. Willoughby, who are already veterinarians. Many others, like Mr. Kamen, stay within the law by working on animals free of charge, usually for friends or human patients. Some states allow chiropractors to work with animals on a veterinarian's referral.

But many chiropractors run into trouble. Mr. Hoff, the Trenton chiropractor, says he treated hundreds of horses—until veterinarians got a court order two years ago barring him and other New Jersey chiropractors from working on animals.

Veterinarians say they are just thinking of the animals. Many chiropractors say the vets are just protecting their turf. However, many chiropractors also urge caution. "Personally, I think we need more validation of these procedures for animals," says Donald L. Harris, the executive vice president of the American Chiropractic Association—who himself occasionally has practiced chiropractic on animals when a veterinarian requested it. He says the association supports veterinary chiropractic to the extent it is permitted "but wouldn't support it where it is prohibited."

The debate over the usefulness of chiropractic for animals doesn't help members of a profession that has suffered decades of derision. In Davenport, Iowa, medical students used to drive by Palmer College of Chiropractic jeering, "Quack, quack, quack,"[1] Dr. Willoughby says.

The field began in 1895, when Daniel David Palmer, the

---

[1] **Author's Note:** Dr. Hank Kostecki, a very gifted and skilled holistic veterinarian who practices in South Lake Tahoe, California, relayed the following explanation of the origin of the term "quack" as used to describe a person, such as a fraudulent doctor, who pretends to have curative powers. Dr. Kostecki explains: "As recently as 100 years ago, standard, allopathic doctors (M.D.'s) treated an enormous number of conditions with mercury which caused sweating, chills, etc. from its own toxicity. These symptoms were erroneously seen as some causative principle being driven out of the body. This practice caused untold suffering and worsening, naturally, and in addition to blood letting is what killed George Washington. Villagers in Europe were terrified of the M.D.'s and sought the services of those "wise women" versed in herbology who literally risked their lives to provide their art. The German word for Mercury is pronounced "Quack-Salber," (spelled *Quecksilber*). People of that era then came to fear what they called the "Quacks." So the above students in the *Wall St. Journal* article are really referring to themselves and their predecessors."

father of chiropractic, performed the historic first adjustment in Davenport. He founded Palmer College, now the world's largest chiropractic school. His premise was that the displacement of vertebrae can interfere with nerves, disrupt the body's functioning and produce numerous ailments.

For years, the profession suffered from exaggerated cure-all claims of some early enthusiasts. But it has gradually gained much more acceptance. As part of a court case settlement last month, the American Hospital Association recently dropped its objection to giving chiropractors rights to practice in hospitals.

But nothing was said about, say, admitting a goat with a sore back to the emergency room.

## Appendix C

# Where to Find Animal Chiropractors

Believe it or not, the question this chapter asks is not an easy one to answer. There aren't many full-time animal chiropractors. So who do you turn to when you need help with a method, or simply want someone more experienced to perform a particular procedure?

For years, I've been conducting seminars around the U.S., training chiropractors and veterinarians in animal chiropractic. The success of this book has also helped put me in touch with other practitioners who developed these skills on their own. As a result, we have been developing a national register of practitioners of animal chiropractic. At the back of this book, you will find a request form for a free directory of practitioners who have agreed to be listed—*and* to honor a coupon (enclosed with your directory) which will entitle your dog to a *free adjustment*. See p. 166 for details on this unbeatable deal!

For additional copies of the directory, you can write to me at 3421 N. Arlington Heights Rd., Arlington Heights, IL 60004 (include a self-addressed stamped envelope); call my office at 1-800-742-8433; e-mail me at <kamen@miint.net>; or access my web page: http://www.miint.net/~kamen/

# BIBLIOGRAPHY

Carlson, Delbert G. and Giffen, James M. *Dog Owner's Home Veterinary Handbook*; Howell Book House, 1980.

Cole, Joanna. *A Dog's Body*; William Morrow and Co., Inc. 1986.

Galinis, Michael R. "A Chiropractic Approach to Veterinary Problems"; *The Digest of Chiropractic Economics*, January/February 1980.

Gatterman, Meridel I. *Chiropractic Managment of Spine-Related Disorders*; Williams & Wilkins 1990.

Getty, Robert. *The Anatomy of the Domestic Animals*; W. B. Saunders Company 1975.

Kay, William J. *The Complete Book of Dog Health*; Macmillan Publishing Company 1985.

McGinnis, Terri. *The Well Dog Book*; Random House 1974.

Medford, Myles A. "Veterinary Chiropractic: Feasible, Practical and Proves Chiropractic Premise"; *Digest of Chiropractic Economics*, November/December 1980 (part 1) and January/February 1981 (part 2).

Miller, Malcolm E. *Anatomy of the Dog*; W.B. Saunders Company 1964.

Miller, Malcom E. *Guide To The Dissection Of The Dog* (third edition); New York State Veterinary College 1955.

Oliver, John E. and Lorenz, Michael D. *Handbook of Veterinary Neurology*; W.B. Saunders Company 1993.

Schafer, R.C. *Chiropractic Management of Sports and Recreational Injuries*; Williams & Wilkins 1986.

Stephenson, R.W. *Chiropractic Text Book*; Palmer School of Chiropractic 1927.

Whittick, William G. *Canine Orthopedics*; Lea & Febiger 1990.

# INDEX

# ABOUT THE AUTHOR

**Dr. Daniel Kamen** was born on June 18th, 1956, in Chicago, Illinois. He has been practicing chiropractic since 1981. His father is a highly respected anesthesiologist; his mother, a gifted artist. Dr. Kamen's original animal chiropractic organization, "Animal Crackers," produced animal chiropractic educational materials, which taught others how to adjust dogs and horses.

Dr. Kamen lives with his wife, Sharon, of eighteen years, along with their three sons, Jeffrey, Gary and Kevin. He makes his home in Buffalo Grove, Illinois. Dr. Kamen has been featured on many TV, radio, and newspaper stories concerning his work with animal chiropractic. He currently is on tour, teaching a professional as well as a lay lecture seminar on animal chiropractic (horse and dog adjusting). His hobbies include playing the piano and chess (master level).

# MARKETPLACE

1. **Video** on animal adjusting (dogs and horses). This 90-minute video demonstrates all of the canine methods described in this book, as well as how to adjust horses! Anatomy as well as adjusting techniques are covered in the video. $49.95 plus $3.50 S&H. Illinois residents include 8-1/4% sales tax ($4.12).

2. **Metal mallet.** $139.00 (lowest price available) plus $3.00 S&H. Illinois residents add 8-1/4% sales tax ($11.47). If both the video and mallet are bought together, add only $3.00 total for S&H.

*Send check to:*
Kamen Chiropractic
3421 N. Arlington Heights Road
Arlington Heights, IL 60004
*or call* 1-800-742-8433

# FREE OFFER!

Return the form below to receive a FREE national directory of practitioners of animal chiropractic, plus a coupon for ONE FREE ADJUSTMENT for your pet! Mail to:

Attn: Directory Offer
Brookline Books
P.O. Box 1047
Cambridge, MA 02238-1047

---

Dear Brookline Books,

I am interested in professional chiropractic care for my dog. Please send me a FREE national directory of chiropractors and veterinarians who offer this service, along with a coupon for ONE FREE ADJUSTMENT from a participating practitioner.

Name _____

Address _____

_____

City _____

State _____ ZIP _____ — _____

---

*Limit one free-adjustment coupon per customer or household. Reproductions of this request form will not be honored. Services may not be available in all areas; listing in the directory does not guarantee participation by an individual practitioner. Void where prohibited by law.*